The greatest doodle pads €

THE Procrastinator®

Notebook

The essential everyday companion

A notebook with not only plenty
of space for making notes about all
the things you have to make notes
about, but also page after page of
scribbles, choices, lists, decisions
and other nonsense to fill in when
things get really boring.

Published by Production Line Limited
ISBN 978-1-906356-05-7

Gallery

Nice Tie

Preferences 1-10

- [ ] Potatoes
- [ ] Cauliflower
- [ ] Peas
- [ ] Sweetcorn
- [ ] Carrots
- [ ] Sprouts
- [ ] Aubergines
- [ ] Cabbage
- [ ] Parsnips
- [ ] Broccoli

Sod's Law

I've apparently installed the wrong software, the printer's jammed and now that knob thing's dropped off.

Suggestions box

A better colour for St Paul's Cathedral

Magnolia [ ]

Burnt Umber [ ]

Reasons to be cheerful

1 _____

2 _____

3 _____

Quarter final draw

[ ]	V	[ ]
[ ]	V	[ ]
[ ]	V	[ ]
[ ]	V	[ ]

Definitive definitions

[ ] (adj) Body appearance after a very long bath

[ ] (n) Loose strands of hair covering a bald patch

[ ] (v) Talking with a mouth full of crisps

Join the dots

Weather report

Yesterday _____

Today _____

Tomorrow _____

Tonight's bedtime

12
9   3
6

Uproar

There was absolute chaos in Parliament earlier today when someone shouted out...

[ ]

Dilemmas

Visiting the relatives this weekend

Bob's your uncle ☐

Fanny's your aunt ☐

The void

Resolutions already broken

1 _____

2 _____

3 _____

Spatial awareness

The first half

Action

Hotel

Treasure

The latest fall of snow

Preferences 1-10

☐ Spiders
☐ Moths
☐ Flies
☐ Fleas
☐ Bees
☐ Wasps
☐ Beetles
☐ Ants
☐ Thrips
☐ Butterflies

Occurrences

There was a big earthquake once, at least thirteen people fell off their bicycles and some of the sea is going to evaporate.

The big deal

It would be really good if Sir Richard Branson popped in and asked for help with the...

Chill gauge

Coolish   Sub-sub zero

An embarrassing moment

Doublers

Ways of keeping warm during a cold snap

Charting progress - Caffeine intake

Strong Cups

Mon   Tues   Wed   Thurs   Fri

The Bank

The Bunkers

The
Copse

Tee Off

Aren't they marvellous?

Your rash has just turned bright green, but they can't give you an appointment until a week Thursday.

Slug

Jelly

Toad

Charles. *Entering stage left with the ladder.*

Felicity. *From the shower with menace and feeling.*

Charles.

Felicity! (loudly).........

....

Charles....................

....

Ah............................

Eating

Sleeping

Arguing

Shouting

Working

Shaking

Drinking

Running

Walking

Falling

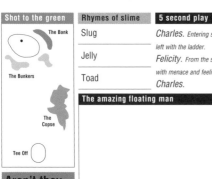

A finger of fudge is just enough

Agree

Disagree

As a first priority, measure the door of your office to ensure you can leave at the end of the day without calling for assistance.

One Man and his

Whatever happened to

Richard and

Saturday Night at

1

2

3

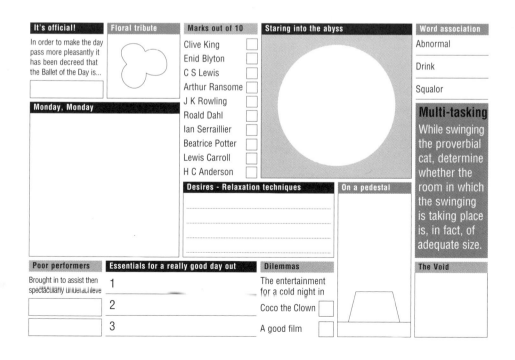

It's official!

In order to make the day pass more pleasantly it has been decreed that the Ballet of the Day is...

Floral tribute

Marks out of 10

Clive King

Enid Blyton

C S Lewis

Arthur Ransome

J K Rowling

Roald Dahl

Ian Serraillier

Beatrice Potter

Lewis Carroll

H C Anderson

Staring into the abyss

Word association

Abnormal

Drink

Squalor

Multi-tasking

While swinging the proverbial cat, determine whether the room in which the swinging is taking place is, in fact, of adequate size.

Monday, Monday

Desires - Relaxation techniques

On a pedestal

Poor performers

Brought in to assist then spectacularly underachieve

Essentials for a really good day out

1

2

3

Dilemmas

The entertainment for a cold night in

Coco the Clown

A good film

The Void

V V

1

2

3

▶

This announcement
followed a review

A bit flush

Not too clever

What's all that about?

Quantum mechanics, the evolution of social inequality and the third button from the left on the video.

Large [   ] falls off back of lorry

MP caught with [   ] in cabinet

Worrying cracks found in [   ]

Woman lifts [   ] to delight crowd

For their outstanding
contribution to lack of
taste and incredibly
bad dress sense...

Richard

Clare

Arthur

☐ Cluedo
☐ Backgammon
☐ Monopoly
☐ Risk
☐ Draughts
☐ Boggle
☐ Chess
☐ Jenga
☐ Trivial Pursuit
☐ The Great I Am

Star turns	Dilemmas	Major issues to be ignored	A 'P' please, Bob	Poles apart

Star turns

Bruce

Lauren

Hank

Dilemmas

Which underwear to wear under

Long johns ☐

A thong ☐

Major issues to be ignored

1

2

3

A 'P' please, Bob

P

Poles apart

Political parties whose views may cause offence

The void

Great events in history

Thought for the day

If you won £15 million on the Lottery, would you be really happy or a big smug git with far too much money.

Daydreaming

Preferences 1-10

☐ Nirvana
☐ Led Zeppelin
☐ Metallica
☐ Kiss
☐ Guns 'n' Roses
☐ Motorhead
☐ Sex Pistols
☐ Iron Maiden
☐ AC/DC
☐ Jimi Hendrix

Join the dots

Price fixing - I bought the company

Date

Pay

The Sum of   £

1345 673 2759 02

Bad behaviour

There was a near riot in the fruit and vegetable market early today when someone shouted out...

The boss

To be considered

Eating the skin off the custard

Possibly ☐

Never again ☐

Recycling

To dispose of this in an environmentally friendly way, scrumple it up into a little ball and flick it across the room, off the wall into the wastebin.

Read all about it

The Daily

Sad face

Pains in the arse

1 _____

2 _____

3 _____

It's only G words

G _____

G _____

G _____

A sledgehammer to crack a nut

_____ to open a can of beans

_____ to get rid of acne

_____ to get from A to B

_____ to relieve insomnia

Planned intake

Volume

Mon Tues Wed Thurs Fri Sat Sun

Just saying

There was a time when all you needed was a pencil and some paper to pass the time.

Planning permission

Marks out of 10

Bungalow ☐

Igloo ☐

Mansion ☐

Condominium ☐

Cave ☐

Semi-detached ☐

Teepee ☐

Flat ☐

Tree House ☐

Detached ☐

Fat

Enemy

North

Andromeda ☐
Charioteer ☐
Great Dog ☐
Furnace ☐
Scales ☐
Unicorn ☐
Easel ☐
Archer ☐
Virgin ☐
Compasses ☐

Awarded to

for their

Signed

1

2

3

Is experimentation
on animals justified?

Never ☐

Only if it hurts ☐

Perfect timing

It was a total
coincidence
that, as Man
decided to go
to the moon,
Woman said
she'd make the
sandwiches.

Ways to travel between
York and Barnsley

There was agreement at
all levels to find a way
of limiting the use of
scissors when cutting...

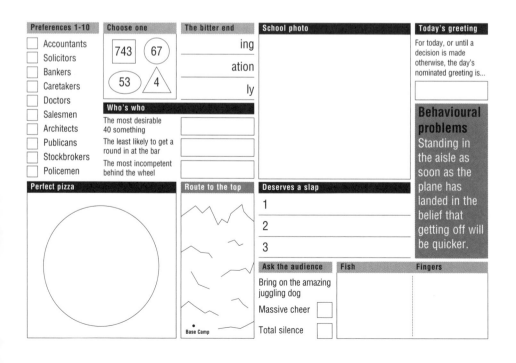

Preferences 1-10

- ☐ Accountants
- ☐ Solicitors
- ☐ Bankers
- ☐ Caretakers
- ☐ Doctors
- ☐ Salesmen
- ☐ Architects
- ☐ Publicans
- ☐ Stockbrokers
- ☐ Policemen

Perfect pizza

Choose one

743   67

53   4

Who's who

The most desirable 40 something

The least likely to get a round in at the bar

The most incompetent behind the wheel

The bitter end

ing

ation

ly

Route to the top

• Base Camp

School photo

Deserves a slap

1

2

3

Ask the audience

Bring on the amazing juggling dog

Massive cheer ☐

Total silence ☐

Fish

Today's greeting

For today, or until a decision is made otherwise, the day's nominated greeting is...

Behavioural problems
Standing in the aisle as soon as the plane has landed in the belief that getting off will be quicker.

Fingers

Preferences 1-10

- [ ] Buddleia
- [ ] Clematis
- [ ] Firethorn
- [ ] Gorse
- [ ] Honeysuckle
- [ ] Laburnum
- [ ] Mock Orange
- [ ] Poinsettia
- [ ] Rock Rose
- [ ] Skimmia

The void

With hindsight

It might well have been better to have asked for warm soapy water and a towel before opening the...

Fantasy day permit

This permit entitles the bearer to

_____

_____

Lasts for one day only

Playing up for the crowd

Dilemmas

Choosing to go on a break in the country

Let's go [ ]

Which country? [ ]

Bones of contention

1 _____

2 _____

3 _____

Egg decorating

Really good things to do

....
....
....
....

Blind Date

Two drama queens who might like the company

[   ]

[   ]

First name terms

Cox
_____

Lewis
_____

Fellows
_____

Things to do

Ask a group of friends to try recreating the final battle scene from _Zulu_ without the fighting or significant loss of life.

Square deal

Definitive definitions

☐ (v) Running in a panic through very wet mud

☐ (adj) Untanned areas of skin after a holiday

☐ (n) The wearer of sunglasses indoors

What's on telly?

Sod's Law

Our villa was double booked by the Webbs, Jan got food poisoning and it turned out to be 'fleece the tourist' fortnight.

Possessions

Sleeping Bag ☐
Kettle ☐
Furry Dice ☐
Suspenders ☐
Lawnmower ☐
Cap ☐
Skateboard ☐
Carriage Clock ☐
Bow Tie ☐
Socket Set ☐

Dr and Mrs Jekyll

Disgusting things

1
2
3

The verdict

Being amused by a family bereavement

Guilty ☐

Not Guilty ☐

Fancy a drink?

You what!?

At the end of the day, when all's said and done and the dust has settled, what really does happen when push comes to shove.

Car badge

Mood swings

Yesterday

Today

Tomorrow

Valuable lessons

☐ x ☐ − ☐ + ☐ ÷ ☐ = ☐

☐ + ☐ ÷ ☐ x ☐ − ☐ = ☐

☐ ÷ ☐ + ☐ − ☐ x ☐ = ☐

A very bad hair day

Movies worth seeing

1

2

3

The void

Dilemmas

Your dinner guest
for the evening

Hannibal Lecter

Gordon Ramsay

Marks out of 10

Ingrid Bergman

Marlon Brando

Nicolas Cage

Richard Dreyfuss

Ava Gardner

Michael Gambon

Audrey Hepburn

Gene Kelly

Steve McQueen

Julia Roberts

An incredibly complicated diagram

The second half

Shower

Ringer

Party

**What a total
waste of time**

Expecting other
motorists to
use the inside
lane of the
motorway
instead of
always staying
in the middle.

Half and half

Thinking ahead

When travelling on the
bus through Hounslow
it is absolutely essential
to pack a really good...

Reality check

Time	Place
Who's in front	
Who's behind	
Who's talking	

Pairing up

A big blue thing and a
very small red thing

Celebrations - A mate's birthday

Worst nightmare

Check the cheque

Date _____

Pay _____

The Sum of _____   £ [   ]

_____

1345 673 2759 02   _____

First thought

Large
_____
Medium
_____
Small

Giant slalom

Start ▼

Finish ■

Preferences 1-10

☐ Truro
☐ Inverness
☐ Caernarfon
☐ Dudley
☐ Basingstoke
☐ Barnsley
☐ South Shields
☐ Haverfordwest
☐ Plymouth
☐ Blackpool

Where am I going?

Travel guide

A likely destination for the next holiday

Bermuda [   ]

Southend [   ]

Tonight Matthew...

I am going to squeeze myself into a slinky little black mini, pretend to be talented, and be...

[   ]

Difficult circumstances

1 _____

2 _____

3 _____

Pig face

• •

Appearing in the Big Top

The Fellini Brothers and their [   ]

Alfredo Ponzo's [   ]

The Human [   ] and Delores

Wacky Walter with [   ]

Aren't they marvellous?

They managed to get me off with a caution and all for the cost of funding the US space programme.

Small

Top

Creepy

Today's the day

For considering all the things you were going to do this weekend and then putting them off yet again.

The void

Disappearing into the distance

Headlines

The Daily
NEWS

Preferences 1-10

☐ Broad Bean
☐ Soya Bean
☐ Blackeyed Bean
☐ French Bean
☐ Haricot Bean
☐ Baked Bean
☐ Runner Bean
☐ Borlotti Bean
☐ Flageolet Bean
☐ Kidney Bean

Bad advice

Dilemmas

A flying visit to Transylvania

Count me in ☐

Pass the garlic ☐

Time out

12
9   3
6

Shattered dreams

Weak personalities

1

2

3

Announcement

Due to unforeseen circumstances Elvis will not be performing and will be replaced by...

Heavy hitters

Rolling around together in a mud wrestling pit

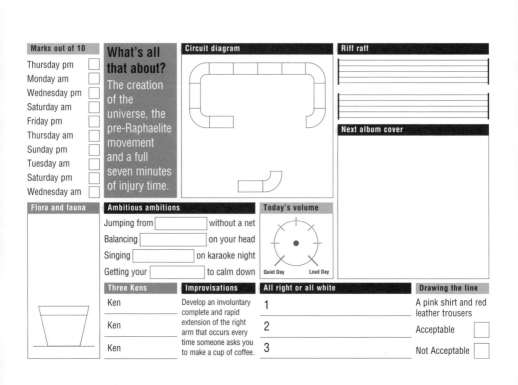

Marks out of 10

Thursday pm ☐
Monday am ☐
Wednesday pm ☐
Saturday am ☐
Friday pm ☐
Thursday am ☐
Sunday pm ☐
Tuesday am ☐
Saturday pm ☐
Wednesday am ☐

What's all that about?

The creation of the universe, the pre-Raphaelite movement and a full seven minutes of injury time.

Circuit diagram

Riff raff

Next album cover

Flora and fauna

Ambitious ambitions

Jumping from ☐ without a net
Balancing ☐ on your head
Singing ☐ on karaoke night
Getting your ☐ to calm down

Today's volume

Quiet Day   Loud Day

Three Kens

Ken
Ken
Ken

Improvisations

Develop an involuntary complete and rapid extension of the right arm that occurs every time someone asks you to make a cup of coffee.

All right or all white

1
2
3

Drawing the line

A pink shirt and red leather trousers
Acceptable ☐
Not Acceptable ☐

Great figures	Epic encounters	Juvenile delinquents		Best mates	Dilemmas

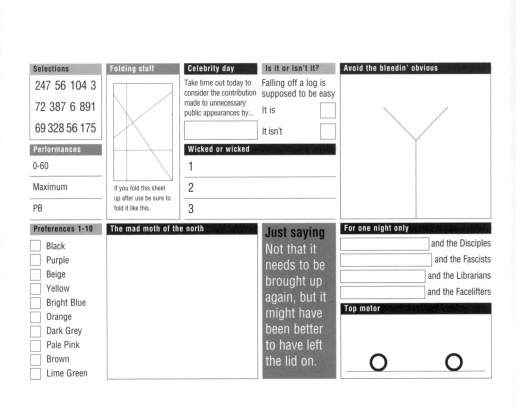

Selections

247 56 104 3

72 387 6 891

69 328 56 175

Performances

0-60

Maximum

PB

Preferences 1-10

- [ ] Black
- [ ] Purple
- [ ] Beige
- [ ] Yellow
- [ ] Bright Blue
- [ ] Orange
- [ ] Dark Grey
- [ ] Pale Pink
- [ ] Brown
- [ ] Lime Green

Folding stuff

If you fold this sheet up after use be sure to fold it like this.

The mad moth of the north

Celebrity day

Take time out today to consider the contribution made to unnecessary public appearances by...

Wicked or wicked

1

2

3

Is it or isn't it?

Falling off a log is supposed to be easy

It is [ ]

It isn't [ ]

Just saying

Not that it needs to be brought up again, but it might have been better to have left the lid on.

Avoid the bleedin' obvious

For one night only

_____ and the Disciples

_____ and the Fascists

_____ and the Librarians

_____ and the Facelifters

Top motor

Stupid things to do

Bizarre animals

1

2

3

Bad timing

On being told they'd arrived a day after the six month deadline the Lottery winner said...

The void

Daily pass

Name

Sex

Mood

Visiting

Custer's last stand

Means the same

Accidental

Malignant

Risqué

Preferences 1-10

☐ Bees
☐ Buffalo
☐ Crocodiles
☐ Dogs
☐ Ferrets
☐ Lions
☐ Owls
☐ Sparrows
☐ Turkeys
☐ Zebras

Choices

Daily newspapers to buy for a train journey

Tonight's telly

◀ ● ▶

That'll be the day!

A machine will be invented that will do all our adding up, subtraction and might even have a go at long division.

Dilemmas

Who would you ask to do your highlights

Nicky Clarke ☐

Sweeney Todd ☐

Shape it up

Mental images

The full blooded golf swing that results in the ball travelling thirty feet at right angles off to the left and chucking up a massive clod of earth.

Behavioural problems

Talking and laughing very loudly in a manner likely to draw attention to oneself.

The living photocopier

Dinner is served

Strange smelling places

1

2

3

Votes of note

What to do with the butter mountain

Wrestle in it ☐

Yodel on it ☐

Today's estimates

Bin Bags

Phone Calls

Close Shaves

Superheroes

Saving the world from bad vibes and heaviness

Fighting the battle against loudness in all its forms

Helping to banish brown sandals from the planet

Tennis ball

Temperature

Marks out of 10

Buses ☐
The Tube ☐
Bicycles ☐
Taxis ☐
Aeroplanes ☐
Trams ☐
Yachts ☐
Trains ☐
Scooters ☐
Ferries ☐

Animal Farm

Did you know

On average more food is eaten by the individuals who consume more than anybody else than by those who eat less.

Mr or Mrs

Hodges

Thomas

Fish

The void

Behind closed doors

Director of petty, spiteful insults and generally putting people down

Marks out of 10

Cannibalism ☐
Communism ☐
Exhibitionism ☐
Feminism ☐
Idealism
Mysticism ☐
Optimism ☐
Realism ☐
Socialism ☐
Tokenism ☐

Basic instincts - Road rage

We're comin' in

Entrance

Running on empty

Two for tea

Two philosophers for cream scones and jam

Empty boxes

The winners in reverse order

1

2

3

Dilemmas

Destinations when travelling in time

US Civil War ☐

Medieval Britain ☐

You don't say

When making your test debut for England against the West Indies don't forget your...

Holiday snap

Preferences 1-10
- Corn Flakes
- Rice Krispies
- Muesli
- Porridge
- Shredded Wheat
- Coco Pops
- Sugar Smacks
- Weetabix
- Frosties
- All Bran

Sod's Law

There was only one ticket counter open, the train's running 40 minutes late and now I'm sat next to the loud child.

Definitive definitions

(*adj*) The hair style that you didn't ask for

(*n*) The beanpole in front of you at the cinema

(*v*) Attempting to contain helpless laughter

From start to finish

Finish

Start

Up the flagpole

Suggestions box

The preferred name for the next King

Roger

Edwin

The Good, the Bad and the Ugly

1

2

3

Perfect matches

____ + ____

____ + ____

____ + ____

____ + ____

Health check

Yesterday

Today

Tomorrow

At the third stroke

Marital bliss

There was an almighty fracas at a society wedding today when the best man was found...

Dilemmas

What to do to run off a little weight

Gentle Jogging ☐

Rollerball ☐

The void

Chewy sweets

1

2

3

Rearranging the room

The Door

The Window

The first half

Opera

Dual

Baggy

Chaos theory

Preferences 1-10

☐ Hillman Imp
☐ S Type Jaguar
☐ Morris Minor
☐ VW Beetle
☐ Ford Mustang
☐ Citroen 2CV
☐ Reliant Robin
☐ Wolsley Hornet
☐ Mini Traveller
☐ Austin 1100

Occurrences

A dam burst, there was a drop a rain and it was mandatory to wear a hat when going to watch a game of football.

The big deal

As the world renowned chemist poured the blue sticky liquid into the test tube he said...

Tedium gauge

Boring   Really, really boring

An embarrassing moment

Doublers

Two incredibly hot curries for a cold night

The long way out

In

Out

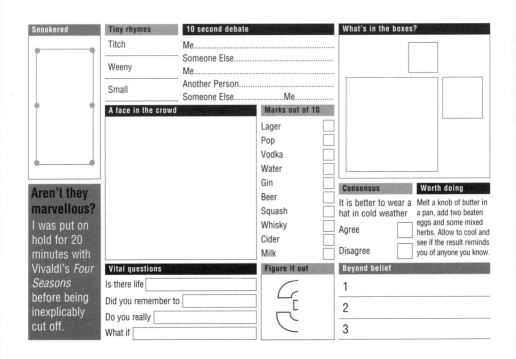

Snookered

Aren't they marvellous?
I was put on hold for 20 minutes with Vivaldi's *Four Seasons* before being inexplicably cut off.

Tiny rhymes
Titch

Weeny

Small

A face in the crowd

Vital questions
Is there life

Did you remember to

Do you really

What if

10 second debate
Me...
Someone Else.................................
Me...
Another Person...............................
Someone Else...................Me................

Marks out of 10
Lager
Pop
Vodka
Water
Gin
Beer
Squash
Whisky
Cider
Milk

Figure it out

What's in the boxes?

Consensus
It is better to wear a hat in cold weather

Agree

Disagree

Worth doing
Melt a knob of butter in a pan, add two beaten eggs and some mixed herbs. Allow to cool and see if the result reminds you of anyone you know.

Beyond belief
1
2
3

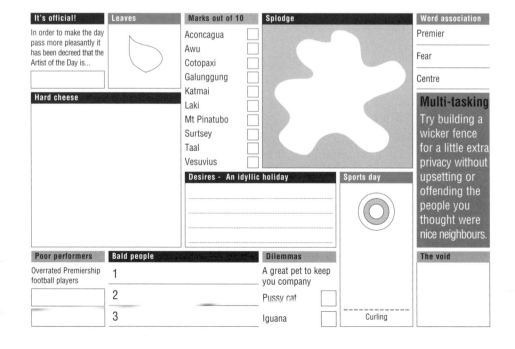

It's official!

In order to make the day pass more pleasantly it has been decreed that the Artist of the Day is...

Hard cheese

Leaves

Marks out of 10

Aconcagua

Awu

Cotopaxi

Galunggung

Katmai

Laki

Mt Pinatubo

Surtsey

Taal

Vesuvius

Splodge

Word association

Premier

Fear

Centre

Multi-tasking

Try building a wicker fence for a little extra privacy without upsetting or offending the people you thought were nice neighbours.

Desires - An idyllic holiday

Sports day

Poor performers

Overrated Premiership football players

Bald people

1

2

3

Dilemmas

A great pet to keep you company

Pussy cat

Iguana

Curling

The void

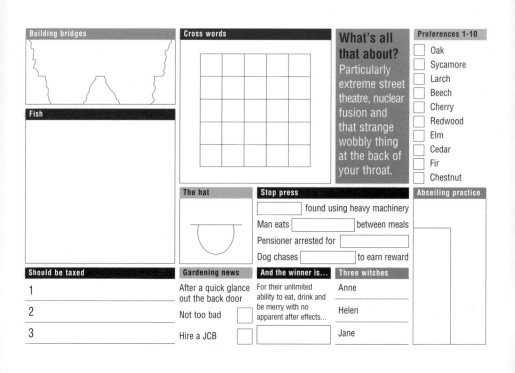

Building bridges

Fish

Should be taxed

1

2

3

Cross words

The hat

Gardening news

After a quick glance
out the back door

Not too bad

Hire a JCB

What's all that about?
Particularly extreme street theatre, nuclear fusion and that strange wobbly thing at the back of your throat.

Stop press

[ ] found using heavy machinery

Man eats [ ] between meals

Pensioner arrested for [ ]

Dog chases [ ] to earn reward

And the winner is...
For their unlimited ability to eat, drink and be merry with no apparent after effects...

Three witches

Anne

Helen

Jane

Preferences 1-10

[ ] Oak
[ ] Sycamore
[ ] Larch
[ ] Beech
[ ] Cherry
[ ] Redwood
[ ] Elm
[ ] Cedar
[ ] Fir
[ ] Chestnut

Abseiling practice

Star turns	Dilemmas	Roads to ruin		Strange	Poles apart

Star turns

Hannah

Ronald

Anne

Dilemmas

Something to wear to cause a stir

Ostrich feathers ☐

A very big hat ☐

Roads to ruin

1

2

3

Strange

Poles apart

Something very big and something very small

☐

☐

The void

Great events in history

Thought for the day

It really is much, much better to receive rather than give, despite what anyone else might say.

Too many cooks

Preferences 1-10

☐ Bandicoot
☐ Boodie
☐ Dibber
☐ Drill
☐ Pygmy Hog
☐ Mink
☐ Woolly Monkey
☐ Pronghorn
☐ Maned Sloth
☐ Woylie

Gazing into the firmament

Some sums

☐ − ☐ − ☐ − ☐ = ☐

☐ + ☐ + ☐ + ☐ = ☐

☐ − ☐ − ☐ − ☐ = ☐

Bad behaviour

There was carnage in the museum earlier today when someone pushed over the...

☐

The exceptionally big thing

To be considered

Diving off the high
board at the pool

Possibly ☐

No Chance ☐

Recycling

When you have finished
with this sheet, place it
in an envelope and pass
it on to someone who
may have need of it for a
more important reason.

Three course meal

1

2

3

Sandwich board

The Big OFFER

Smiley face

It's only P words

P

P

P

Essential equipment

☐ to ward off wild animals

☐ to help with the ironing

☐ to prevent swelling

☐ to remove congestion

Anticipated anxiety

Time in Loo

10.00 11.00 12.00 13.00 14.00 15.00 16.00

Just saying

Well, I know
it's chaos at
the moment
but by the end
of the month
we hope to
have improved
the situation
to a shambles.

Restricted area

Marks out of 10

Lungs ☐

Brain ☐

Tongue ☐

Heart ☐

Spleen ☐

Colon ☐

Liver ☐

Eyes ☐

Kidneys ☐

Appendix ☐

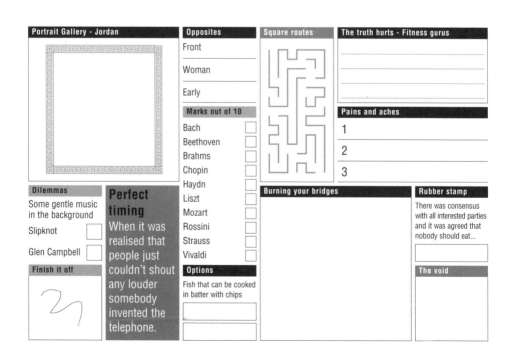

Portrait Gallery - Jordan

Opposites

Front

Woman

Early

Square routes

The truth hurts - Fitness gurus

Marks out of 10

Bach ☐
Beethoven ☐
Brahms ☐
Chopin ☐
Haydn ☐
Liszt ☐
Mozart ☐
Rossini ☐
Strauss ☐
Vivaldi ☐

Pains and aches

1

2

3

Dilemmas

Some gentle music in the background

Slipknot ☐

Glen Campbell ☐

Finish it off

Perfect timing

When it was realised that people just couldn't shout any louder somebody invented the telephone.

Options

Fish that can be cooked in batter with chips

Burning your bridges

Rubber stamp

There was consensus with all interested parties and it was agreed that nobody should eat...

The void

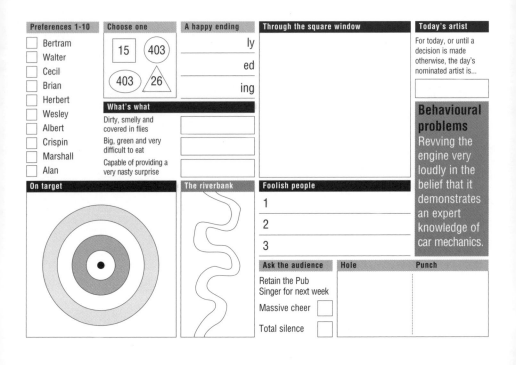

Preferences 1-10

- ☐ Bertram
- ☐ Walter
- ☐ Cecil
- ☐ Brian
- ☐ Herbert
- ☐ Wesley
- ☐ Albert
- ☐ Crispin
- ☐ Marshall
- ☐ Alan

Choose one

15   403
403   26

A happy ending

_____ ly
_____ ed
_____ ing

What's what

Dirty, smelly and covered in flies

Big, green and very difficult to eat

Capable of providing a very nasty surprise

Through the square window

Today's artist

For today, or until a decision is made otherwise, the day's nominated artist is...

Behavioural problems Revving the engine very loudly in the belief that it demonstrates an expert knowledge of car mechanics.

On target

The riverbank

Foolish people

1 _____
2 _____
3 _____

Ask the audience

Retain the Pub Singer for next week

Massive cheer ☐

Total silence ☐

Hole

Punch

Preferences 1-10

- [ ] Algebra
- [ ] Aluminium
- [ ] Acting
- [ ] Adolescence
- [ ] Africa
- [ ] Air
- [ ] Alcohol
- [ ] Animals
- [ ] Antibiotics
- [ ] Archery

The void

Tickets please

Admit One

Gold Club Member   8734 2764 9871 5282

The massive great huge thing

Face painting

Really good things to do

First name terms

Robbins

Walsh

Jackson

Things to do

To make epic sporting encounters slightly less competitive try suggesting that there is no eventual winner.

Blind date

A night out with two of the Village People

Pixelated image

With hindsight

It might well have been better not to have had a skinfull before turning up at the opening of...

Dilemmas

A fashion statement to be proud of

Waistcoat [ ]

Vest [ ]

Jack the lads

1

2

3

Definitive definitions

☐ (*expl, with emphasis*) The call of the wild

☐ (*v*) Biting off more than you can chew

☐ (*v*) Attempting to open a new bin liner

Who's got the remote?

Sod's Law

We'd only just got the stain out following the last incident, and now Stan's girlfriend has managed to do that over it.

Possessions

Camcorder ☐
Spacehopper ☐
Tea Cosy ☐
Blow Heater ☐
Snow Shovel ☐
Earphones ☐
Medallion ☐
Wellies ☐
Driving Gloves ☐
Bradawl ☐

Pond life

New Olympic sports

1 _____

2 _____

3 _____

The verdict

Trying to steal a friend's partner

Guilty ☐

Not Guilty ☐

Same again

You what!?

We're going to build the biggest passenger ship the world has ever seen and tell everyone that it can't be sunk. Then we'll set sail and try it out.

My logo

State of mind

Yesterday _____

Today _____

Tomorrow _____

Score card

1 ☐	2 ☐	3 ☐	4 ☐	5 ☐	6 ☐
7 ☐	8 ☐	9 ☐	10 ☐	11 ☐	12 ☐
13 ☐	14 ☐	15 ☐	16 ☐	17 ☐	18 ☐

The paparazzi strike again

Astronauts

1

2

3

The void

Dilemmas

The quickest way of travelling to Paris

Eurostar ☐

Catapult ☐

Marks out of 10

Marvin Gaye ☐
Simply Red ☐
Pat Boone ☐
Fats Domino ☐
Elvis Presley ☐
The Hollies ☐
Björk ☐
Fleetwood Mac ☐
60ft Dolls ☐
Sister Sledge ☐

Daybreak

The second half

Whistle

Stick

Circus

Half and half

Thinking ahead

When bending down to pick up a coin from the pavement, make sure you've remembered...

Essential activities

This Morning

This Afternoon

This Evening

Pairing up

Two interesting fillings for your open sandwich

Celebrations - Passing the driving test

What a total waste of time

Lying about your age when it is patently clear to just about everyone else just how old you really are.

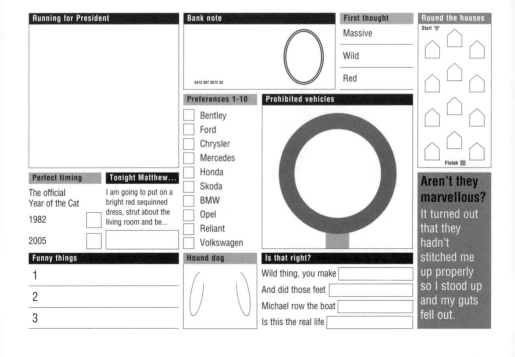

Running for President

Bank note

5413 367 9572 20

First thought

Massive

Wild

Red

Round the houses

Start ▼

Finish ■

Preferences 1-10

- Bentley
- Ford
- Chrysler
- Mercedes
- Honda
- Skoda
- BMW
- Opel
- Reliant
- Volkswagen

Prohibited vehicles

Aren't they marvellous?

It turned out that they hadn't stitched me up properly so I stood up and my guts fell out.

Perfect timing

The official Year of the Cat

1982

2005

Tonight Matthew...

I am going to put on a bright red sequinned dress, strut about the living room and be...

Funny things

1

2

3

Hound dog

Is that right?

Wild thing, you make

And did those feet

Michael row the boat

Is this the real life

Age

Ladies

Shy

Today's the day

For raising the capital required to start that great unfulfilled dream project, however ridiculous it might appear.

The void

All in a day's work

Headlines

The Daily
NEWS

Preferences 1-10

- [ ] Guinea
- [ ] Senegal
- [ ] Sweden
- [ ] Uzbekistan
- [ ] Thailand
- [ ] Morocco
- [ ] Bahrain
- [ ] Mexico
- [ ] Israel
- [ ] Jamaica

Offering advice

Dilemmas

When redecorating the spare room

Rococo

Magnolia

Perfect timing

12

9 ● 3

6

Favourite puddings

1

2

3

Announcement

Because of a total lack of support it has been decided to replace darts on the TV by...

Four windows

Heavy hitters

Two ex world champion heavyweight boxers

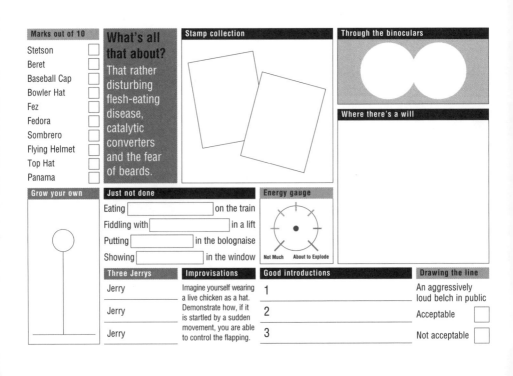

Marks out of 10

- Stetson ☐
- Beret ☐
- Baseball Cap ☐
- Bowler Hat ☐
- Fez ☐
- Fedora ☐
- Sombrero ☐
- Flying Helmet ☐
- Top Hat ☐
- Panama ☐

What's all that about?

That rather disturbing flesh-eating disease, catalytic converters and the fear of beards.

Stamp collection

Through the binoculars

Where there's a will

Grow your own

Just not done

Eating _____ on the train

Fiddling with _____ in a lift

Putting _____ in the bolognaise

Showing _____ in the window

Energy gauge

Not Much   About to Explode

Three Jerrys

Jerry

Jerry

Jerry

Improvisations

Imagine yourself wearing a live chicken as a hat. Demonstrate how, if it is startled by a sudden movement, you are able to control the flapping.

Good introductions

1

2

3

Drawing the line

An aggressively loud belch in public

Acceptable ☐

Not acceptable ☐

Great figures	Epic encounters	Things to die for		Best mates	Dilemmas

Great figures

1 4 7
9 8 5

Epic encounters

French artistic giants of the 19th Century

Things to die for

1

2

3

Best mates

Mandy

Freddie

Nancy

Dilemmas

When conscription could not be avoided

Army ☐

Navy ☐

Falling off a log

It really could happen

Politicians of all persuasions will decide to travel back to the real world after spending time in Cloud Cuckoo Land.

Holding forth - Youngsters of today

Disaster at sea

Marks out of 10

Sputnik 1 ☐
Explorer 1 ☐
Luna 1 ☐
Vostok 1 ☐
Mariner 2 ☐
Gemini 6 ☐
Apollo 8 ☐
Soyuz 5 ☐
Voyager 2 ☐
Viking 1 ☐

Over-reactions

There was no doubt that everyone thought that our lives would be transformed by the...

Important labelling

┌ ─ ─ ─ ─ ─ ─ ─ ─ ─ ─ ─ ┐
│ **Dangerous Chemicals** │
│ │
│ _____ │
│ │
└ ─ ─ ─ ─ ─ ─ ─ ─ ─ ─ ─ ┘

The void

Selections	Top secret	Celebrity day	Is it or isn't it?	Try something different

Selections

442 523 1324

4321 334 325

532 424 4231

Record breakers

Drinks

Fall

Sleep

Preferences 1-10

☐ Piano
☐ Viola
☐ Guitar
☐ French Horn
☐ Trombone
☐ Hurdy-gurdy
☐ Piccolo
☐ Spoons
☐ Saxophone
☐ Euphonium

Top secret

DANGER

This is the button to cause mass destruction and intolerable suffering. **Do not** press unless you feel you've had a particularly bad day.

Celebrity day

Dedicated to those who have no talent or ability of their own, yet somehow achieve fame anyway...

Things to be ashamed of

1

2

3

Is it or isn't it?

Is you is or is you ain't my baby?

You is ☐

You ain't ☐

Try something different

●   ●

Joining the queue

Just saying

You'd have saved yourself about seven minutes if you'd turned right at the lights, first left and past the crematorium.

Defamation

_____ is a smarmy git

_____ smells a lot

_____ can't get anything right

_____ is open to offers

Super superstructure

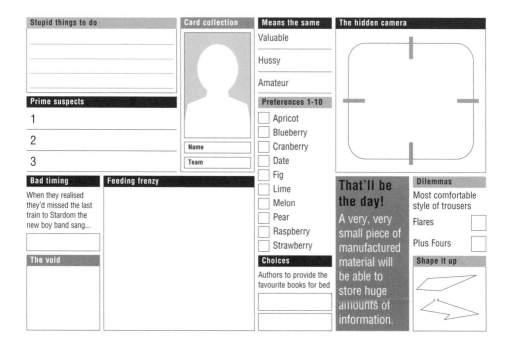

Stupid things to do

....
....
....
....

Prime suspects

1 _____

2 _____

3 _____

Bad timing

When they realised
they'd missed the last
train to Stardom the
new boy band sang...

The void

Feeding frenzy

Card collection

Name

Team

Means the same

Valuable

Hussy

Amateur

Preferences 1-10

☐ Apricot
☐ Blueberry
☐ Cranberry
☐ Date
☐ Fig
☐ Lime
☐ Melon
☐ Pear
☐ Raspberry
☐ Strawberry

Choices

Authors to provide the
favourite books for bed

The hidden camera

**That'll be
the day!**

A very, very
small piece of
manufactured
material will
be able to
store huge
amounts of
information.

Dilemmas

Most comfortable
style of trousers

Flares ☐

Plus Fours ☐

Shape it up

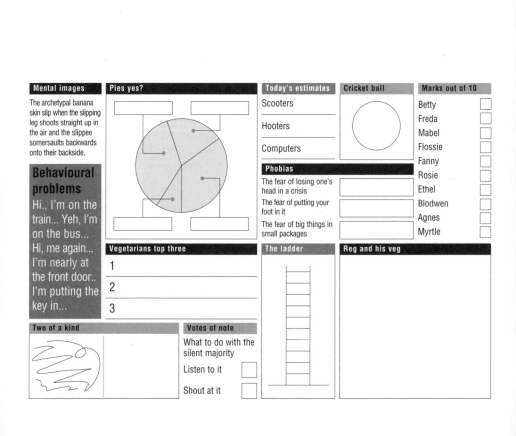

Mental images

The archetypal banana skin slip when the slipping leg shoots straight up in the air and the slippee somersaults backwards onto their backside.

Behavioural problems

Hi.. I'm on the train... Yeh, I'm on the bus... Hi, me again... I'm nearly at the front door.. I'm putting the key in...

Pies yes?

Vegetarians top three

1

2

3

Two of a kind

Votes of note

What to do with the silent majority

Listen to it

Shout at it

Today's estimates

Scooters

Hooters

Computers

Phobias

The fear of losing one's head in a crisis

The fear of putting your foot in it

The fear of big things in small packages

The ladder

Cricket ball

Marks out of 10

Betty

Freda

Mabel

Flossie

Fanny

Rosie

Ethel

Blodwen

Agnes

Myrtle

Reg and his veg

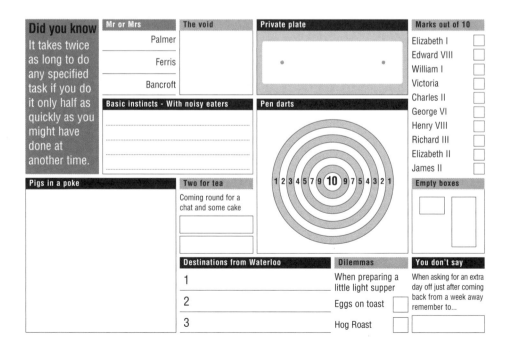

Did you know

It takes twice as long to do any specified task if you do it only half as quickly as you might have done at another time.

Mr or Mrs

Palmer

Ferris

Bancroft

Basic instincts - With noisy eaters

Pigs in a poke

The void

Two for tea

Coming round for a chat and some cake

Private plate

Pen darts

1 2 3 4 5 7 9 **10** 9 7 5 4 3 2 1

Marks out of 10

Elizabeth I ☐
Edward VIII ☐
William I ☐
Victoria ☐
Charles II ☐
George VI ☐
Henry VIII ☐
Richard III ☐
Elizabeth II ☐
James II ☐

Empty boxes

Destinations from Waterloo

1

2

3

Dilemmas

When preparing a little light supper

Eggs on toast ☐

Hog Roast ☐

You don't say

When asking for an extra day off just after coming back from a week away remember to...

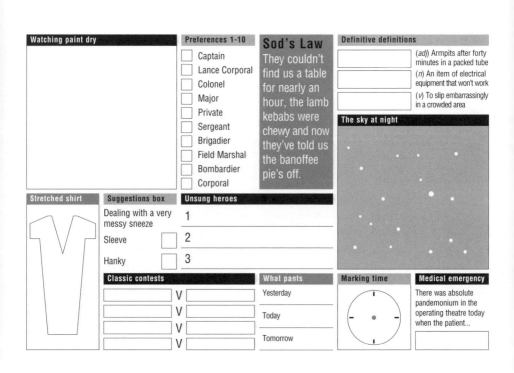

Watching paint dry

Preferences 1-10
- ☐ Captain
- ☐ Lance Corporal
- ☐ Colonel
- ☐ Major
- ☐ Private
- ☐ Sergeant
- ☐ Brigadier
- ☐ Field Marshal
- ☐ Bombardier
- ☐ Corporal

Sod's Law
They couldn't find us a table for nearly an hour, the lamb kebabs were chewy and now they've told us the banoffee pie's off.

Definitive definitions
- (*adj*) Armpits after forty minutes in a packed tube
- (*n*) An item of electrical equipment that won't work
- (*v*) To slip embarrassingly in a crowded area

The sky at night

Stretched shirt

Suggestions box
Dealing with a very messy sneeze

Sleeve ☐

Hanky ☐

Unsung heroes
1
2
3

Classic contests

☐	V	☐
☐	V	☐
☐	V	☐
☐	V	☐

What pants
Yesterday

Today

Tomorrow

Marking time

Medical emergency
There was absolute pandemonium in the operating theatre today when the patient...

Dilemmas	The void	Melons	Planning the attack

Dilemmas

Checking whether to shave armpits

Quite smooth ☐

What a jungle ☐

The void

Melons

1 _____

2 _____

3 _____

Planning the attack

The Village

The River

The Clifftop Lookout

The first half

Cinema

Race

Window

A basket case

Preferences 1-10

☐ Amsterdam
☐ Sydney
☐ Chicago
☐ Vancouver
☐ Prague
☐ Seoul
☐ Milan
☐ Wellington
☐ Jakarta
☐ Honolulu

Occurrences

A riot erupted but nobody really got hurt, someone threw an egg at the Tzar and beer was tuppence in a quart pot.

The big deal

As Blue Watch returned to base after attending another burnt toast incident they said...

Pain gauge

Low   Ahhhhh!

An embarrassing moment

Doublers

Very stylish methods of transport to be seen in

Mirror image

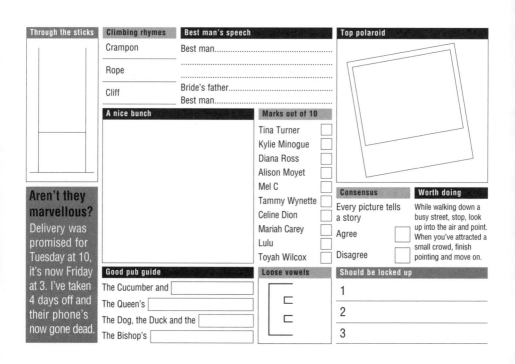

Through the sticks

Climbing rhymes

Crampon

Rope

Cliff

Aren't they marvellous? Delivery was promised for Tuesday at 10, it's now Friday at 3. I've taken 4 days off and their phone's now gone dead.

Best man's speech

Best man..
....
....
Bride's father..
Best man..

A nice bunch

Marks out of 10

Tina Turner ☐
Kylie Minogue ☐
Diana Ross ☐
Alison Moyet ☐
Mel C ☐
Tammy Wynette ☐
Celine Dion ☐
Mariah Carey ☐
Lulu ☐
Toyah Wilcox ☐

Good pub guide

The Cucumber and ☐
The Queen's ☐
The Dog, the Duck and the ☐
The Bishop's ☐

Top polaroid

Consensus

Every picture tells a story

Agree ☐

Disagree ☐

Worth doing

While walking down a busy street, stop, look up into the air and point. When you've attracted a small crowd, finish pointing and move on.

Loose vowels

⊏
⊏

Should be locked up

1 _____
2 _____
3 _____

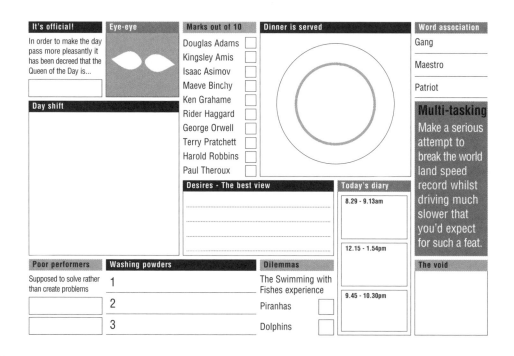

It's official!

In order to make the day pass more pleasantly it has been decreed that the Queen of the Day is...

Eye-eye

Day shift

Marks out of 10

Douglas Adams ☐
Kingsley Amis ☐
Isaac Asimov ☐
Maeve Binchy ☐
Ken Grahame ☐
Rider Haggard ☐
George Orwell ☐
Terry Pratchett ☐
Harold Robbins ☐
Paul Theroux ☐

Desires - The best view

Dinner is served

Today's diary

8.29 - 9.13am

12.15 - 1.54pm

9.45 - 10.30pm

Word association

Gang

Maestro

Patriot

Multi-tasking

Make a serious attempt to break the world land speed record whilst driving much slower that you'd expect for such a feat.

The void

Poor performers

Supposed to solve rather than create problems

Washing powders

1

2

3

Dilemmas

The Swimming with Fishes experience

Piranhas ☐

Dolphins ☐

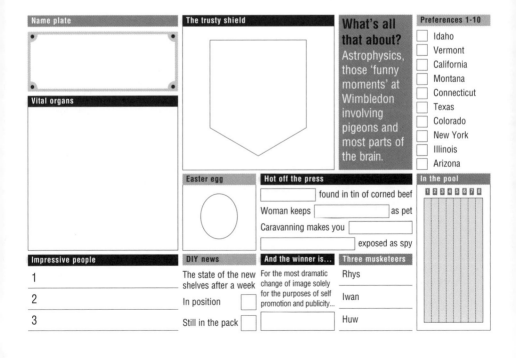

Name plate

Vital organs

Impressive people

1

2

3

The trusty shield

Easter egg

DIY news

The state of the new shelves after a week

In position

Still in the pack

Hot off the press

[   ] found in tin of corned beef

Woman keeps [   ] as pet

Caravanning makes you [   ]

[   ] exposed as spy

And the winner is...

For the most dramatic change of image solely for the purposes of self promotion and publicity...

What's all that about?

Astrophysics, those 'funny moments' at Wimbledon involving pigeons and most parts of the brain.

Three musketeers

Rhys

Iwan

Huw

Preferences 1-10

☐ Idaho
☐ Vermont
☐ California
☐ Montana
☐ Connecticut
☐ Texas
☐ Colorado
☐ New York
☐ Illinois
☐ Arizona

In the pool

1 2 3 4 5 6 7 8

Star turns	Dilemmas	Shades of green	Gee up	Poles apart

Star turns

Steve

Josie

Casey

Dilemmas

The first, vital drink of the day

Hot coffee ☐

Cold vodka ☐

Shades of green

1

2

3

Gee up

G

Poles apart

Regimes that could not possibly co-exist

☐

☐

The void

Great events in history

....
....
....
....
....

Thought for the day

Apparently all's well that ends well - unless getting to the end was truly an absolute bitch and a half.

Dream machine

Preferences 1-10

☐ Cambridgeshire
☐ Cumbria
☐ Devon
☐ Gloucestershire
☐ Lancashire
☐ Northumberland
☐ Shropshire
☐ Suffolk
☐ West Sussex
☐ Worcestershire

The route from A to B

A

B

Behind you!

Bad behaviour

There was pandemonium in the panda house early yesterday when the pandas tried to...

Organised chaos

To be considered

Giving the boss a piece of your mind

Maybe ☐

Not in this life ☐

Recycling

When you have finished with this sheet, carefully remove it from the pad, fold it neatly into a square and hand it to a ticket collector to be checked.

Today's offer

FOR SALE

Long face

When I win the lottery

1 _____

2 _____

3 _____

It's only F words

F _____

F _____

F _____

That's the way to do it

☐ to clear the drains

☐ to prevent hair loss

☐ to occupy children

☐ to create mayhem

Just saying

You can't rely on the weather for holidays in this country. If you'd gone abroad at least you would have had two weeks of sun.

Plotting the plot

Planned consumption

Burgers

Mon Tues Wed Thurs Fri Sat Sun

Marks out of 10

Jay ☐

Sparrow ☐

Tit ☐

Wren ☐

Puffin ☐

Eagle ☐

Bustard ☐

Robin ☐

Lark ☐

Starling ☐

Portrait gallery - Albert Einstein

Opposites

Ugly

Famine

Slow

Favourites menu

Starter

Main Course

Dessert

The truth hurts - Little yappy dogs

....

....

....

....

Marks out of 10

Professor ☐
Rabbi ☐
Mayor ☐
Pope ☐
Duke ☐
Ambassador ☐
Doctor ☐
Marquess ☐
Cardinal ☐
Baron ☐

Crimes of the century

1

2

3

Dilemmas

When slipping into something comfy

Dressing gown ☐

Bondage gear ☐

Finish it off

Perfect timing

The pen was pretty useless at first until it was proposed that some bluey black stuff should go inside.

Options

Ways of dealing with an awkward stain

Frying tonight

Rubber stamp

It is only a matter of time before there is a complete and total ban on computers that...

The void

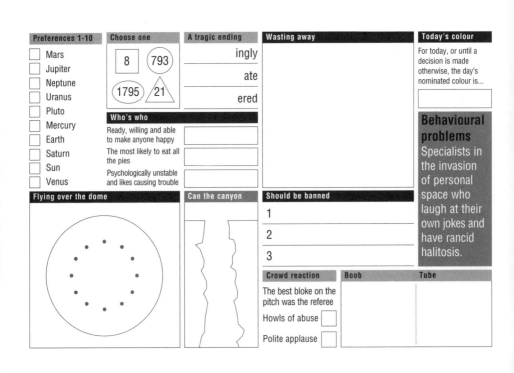

Preferences 1-10

- [ ] Mars
- [ ] Jupiter
- [ ] Neptune
- [ ] Uranus
- [ ] Pluto
- [ ] Mercury
- [ ] Earth
- [ ] Saturn
- [ ] Sun
- [ ] Venus

Choose one

8 793
1795 21

A tragic ending

ingly

ate

ered

Who's who

Ready, willing and able to make anyone happy

The most likely to eat all the pies

Psychologically unstable and likes causing trouble

Wasting away

Today's colour

For today, or until a decision is made otherwise, the day's nominated colour is...

Behavioural problems
Specialists in the invasion of personal space who laugh at their own jokes and have rancid halitosis.

Flying over the dome

Can the canyon

Should be banned

1

2

3

Crowd reaction

The best bloke on the pitch was the referee

Howls of abuse

Polite applause

Boob

Tube

Preferences 1-10

- [ ] Ball
- [ ] Buffett
- [ ] Coombes
- [ ] Fox
- [ ] Hoare
- [ ] Watkins
- [ ] Minto
- [ ] Evans
- [ ] Seal
- [ ] Tebby

The void

Fantasy air ticket

This ticket enables

to fly out, with a few mates, to

Gorilla warfare

Cheesy grin

First name terms

King

Vaughan

Chorley

Really good things to do

Things to do

Trying to make something that is essentially very simple appear much too difficult and really far too hard for a mere human.

Blind date

A night out for Mr Twee and Mrs Assertive

Set squares

With hindsight

When you washed that nice new white shirt, it might have been better not to put it in with...

Dilemmas

Is the visit to the Doctor worthwhile?

It's a sniffle [ ]

Full blown flu [ ]

Channel Islands

1

2

3

Definitive definitions

	(v) Whistling in a loud and tuneless manner
	(adj) Excessively intimate moments in a film
	(n) Broth spoilt by too many cooks

Turn it over

Sod's Law

I was all set for a quiet day on Sunday but now Bev's invited over all of her living relatives for a 'bit of a knees up'.

Possessions

Plasters ☐
Cheese Plant ☐
Fireplace ☐
Sun Lounger ☐
Diary ☐
Large Candle ☐
Duvet ☐
Garden Trowel ☐
Superglue ☐
Old Suit ☐

Just around the corner

20th century women

1
2
3

The verdict

Have considered selling grandmother

Guilty ☐

Not guilty ☐

Pocket aerobatics

You what!?

We'll visit people's homes, suggest some stylish and contemporary ideas for their bedroom and then make them appallingly badly out of MDF.

Sports logo

Willing to listen

Yesterday

Today

Tomorrow

Did you get the registration?

Holiday snaps	Red, red wines		The void	Dilemmas

Red, red wines

1 _____

2 _____

3 _____

Dilemmas

Putting the rubbish out the night before

Dogs and rats ☐

It'll get nicked ☐

Marks out of 10	Dishing the dirt	The second half

Marks out of 10

Coral sea ☐
Arabian Sea ☐
Bering Sea ☐
Hudson Bay ☐
Sea of Japan .
Kara Sea ☐
North Sea ☐
Red Sea ☐
Baltic Sea ☐
Bay of Bengal ☐

The second half

Biscuit

Load

Wheel

Half and half

Thinking ahead

When meeting the boss for lunch to discuss possible promotion opportunities wear a...

What a total waste of time

Trying to argue that black is white when everyone else can clearly see that it is red with blue spots and green bits.

Instant favourites

Cereal

Holiday

Actor

Pairing up

A hard yellow thing and a soft big orange thing

Celebrations - A lottery win

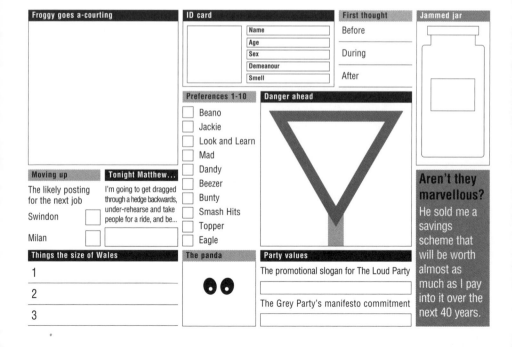

Froggy goes a-courting

ID card

Name	
Age	
Sex	
Demeanour	
Smell	

First thought

Before

During

After

Jammed jar

Preferences 1-10

☐ Beano
☐ Jackie
☐ Look and Learn
☐ Mad
☐ Dandy
☐ Beezer
☐ Bunty
☐ Smash Hits
☐ Topper
☐ Eagle

Danger ahead

Moving up

The likely posting for the next job

Swindon ☐

Milan ☐

Tonight Matthew...

I'm going to get dragged through a hedge backwards, under-rehearse and take people for a ride, and be...

Things the size of Wales

1 _____

2 _____

3 _____

The panda

Party values

The promotional slogan for The Loud Party

_____

The Grey Party's manifesto commitment

_____

Aren't they marvellous?

He sold me a savings scheme that will be worth almost as much as I pay into it over the next 40 years.

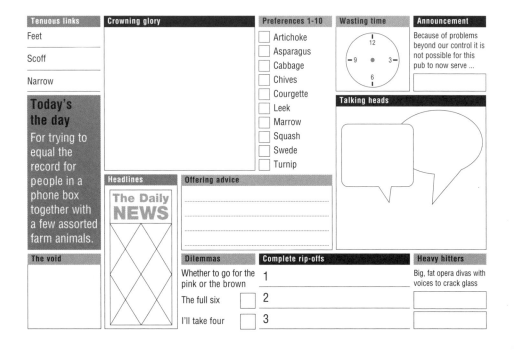

Tenuous links

Feet

Scoff

Narrow

Today's the day

For trying to equal the record for people in a phone box together with a few assorted farm animals.

The void

Crowning glory

Headlines

The Daily
NEWS

Preferences 1-10

- Artichoke
- Asparagus
- Cabbage
- Chives
- Courgette
- Leek
- Marrow
- Squash
- Swede
- Turnip

Offering advice

Dilemmas

Whether to go for the pink or the brown

The full six

I'll take four

Complete rip-offs

1

2

3

Wasting time

12
9   3
6

Talking heads

Announcement

Because of problems beyond our control it is not possible for this pub to now serve ...

Heavy hitters

Big, fat opera divas with voices to crack glass

Marks out of 10

- Sooty ☐
- Gordon the Gopher ☐
- Punch ☐
- Basil Brush ☐
- Sweep ☐
- Andy Pandy ☐
- Roland Rat ☐
- Zippy ☐
- Spit the Dog ☐
- Zag ☐

What's all that about?

A supernova, DNA and the family who insists on sitting right next to you on a deserted beach.

Fantasy Island

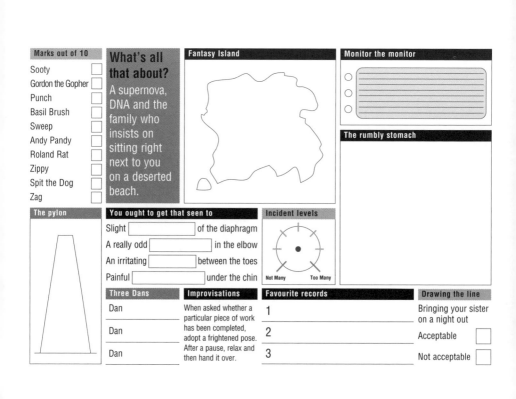

Monitor the monitor

The rumbly stomach

The pylon

You ought to get that seen to

- Slight [   ] of the diaphragm
- A really odd [   ] in the elbow
- An irritating [   ] between the toes
- Painful [   ] under the chin

Incident levels

Not Many   Too Many

Three Dans

Dan
_____
Dan
_____
Dan

Improvisations

When asked whether a particular piece of work has been completed, adopt a frightened pose. After a pause, relax and then hand it over.

Favourite records

1
2
3

Drawing the line

Bringing your sister on a night out
_____
Acceptable ☐

Not acceptable ☐

Great figures	Epic encounters	Vicious cats		Best mates	Dilemmas

Great figures

7 9 3
6 9

Epic encounters

Two enquiring minds who want to enquire

Vicious cats

1 _____

2 _____

3 _____

Best mates

Reginald

Gertrude

David

Dilemmas

The best type of bike to beat the traffic

Chopper ☐

Penny Farthing ☐

Something very strange indeed

It really could happen

Performers in the music industry will be known for their ability to write, sing and play their instruments.

Holding forth - On traffic jams

....

....

....

....

In the forest

Marks out of 10

Angler Fish ☐
Brill ☐
Cod ☐
Flying Fish ☐
Goat Fish ☐
Halibut ☐
Puffer ☐
Salmon ☐
Turbot ☐
Wrasse ☐

Over-reactions

The latest album by the Eurovision Song contest winners was eagerly awaited, but was...

Forged signatures

Signed

_____

Name in Block Capitals

The void

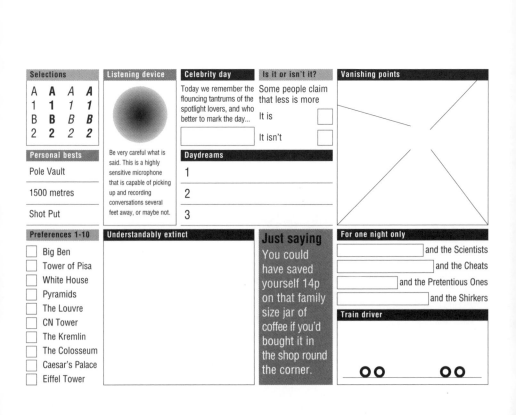

Selections

A **A** *A* *A*
1 **1** *1* *1*
B **B** *B* *B*
2 **2** *2* *2*

Personal bests

Pole Vault

1500 metres

Shot Put

Listening device

Be very careful what is said. This is a highly sensitive microphone that is capable of picking up and recording conversations several feet away, or maybe not.

Celebrity day

Today we remember the flouncing tantrums of the spotlight lovers, and who better to mark the day...

Is it or isn't it?

Some people claim that less is more

It is

It isn't

Daydreams

1

2

3

Vanishing points

Preferences 1-10

☐ Big Ben
☐ Tower of Pisa
☐ White House
☐ Pyramids
☐ The Louvre
☐ CN Tower
☐ The Kremlin
☐ The Colosseum
☐ Caesar's Palace
☐ Eiffel Tower

Understandably extinct

Just saying

You could have saved yourself 14p on that family size jar of coffee if you'd bought it in the shop round the corner.

For one night only

and the Scientists

and the Cheats

and the Pretentious Ones

and the Shirkers

Train driver

OO   OO

Stupid things to do

....

....

....

....

Gone but not forgotten

1

2

3

Bad timing

As the train could be
seen heading out of the
station the frustrated
commuter screamed...

The void

Behind the times

Official licence

Name

Licence

Purpose

Means the same

Senior

Father

Calf

Preferences 1-10

☐ Hunting Dogs
☐ Centaur
☐ Hercules
☐ Fly
☐ Phoenix
☐ Sculptor
☐ Great Bear
☐ Serpent
☐ Wolf
☐ Shield

Choices

Ideal companions for a
nice weekend break

The long lens

That'll be the day!

Small, hard,
round things
that we try to
swallow when
we're feeling
ill will make us
feel an awful
lot better.

Dilemmas

Whether or not to
pay your TV licence

Nothing on TV ☐

Better had ☐

Shape it up

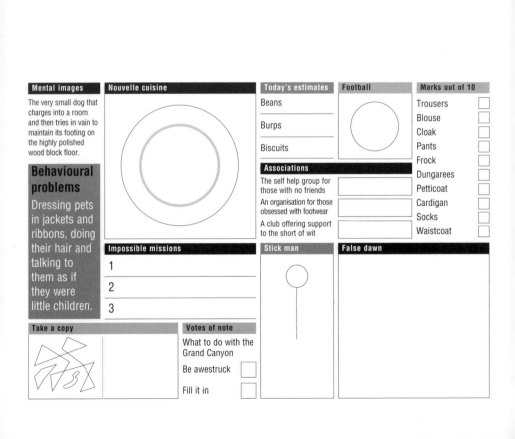

Mental images

The very small dog that charges into a room and then tries in vain to maintain its footing on the highly polished wood block floor.

Behavioural problems

Dressing pets in jackets and ribbons, doing their hair and talking to them as if they were little children.

Nouvelle cuisine

Take a copy

Impossible missions

1

2

3

Votes of note

What to do with the Grand Canyon

Be awestruck

Fill it in

Today's estimates

Beans

Burps

Biscuits

Associations

The self help group for those with no friends

An organisation for those obsessed with footwear

A club offering support to the short of wit

Football

Stick man

False dawn

Marks out of 10

Trousers

Blouse

Cloak

Pants

Frock

Dungarees

Petticoat

Cardigan

Socks

Waistcoat

Did you know

You can usually achieve a lot more if you're motivated and enthusiastic than if you're a bit of a slob who does nothing all day.

Mr or Mrs

Rice

Hubbard

Desmond

Basic instincts - On being overcharged

Crash and burn

The void

Two for tea

Big eaters to stock up on supplies for

Types of bee

1

2

3

Name plate

Finding the spot

Dilemmas

What mood to arrive in work today

Quite pleasant

Don't touch me!

Marks out of 10

Afro ☐
Ponytail ☐
Bouffant ☐
Mullet ☐
Beehive ☐
Mohican ☐
Crew Cut ☐
Quiff ☐
Pageboy ☐
Dreadlocks ☐

Empty boxes

You don't say

If you are going to try a spot of sky diving this weekend don't forget to take along your...

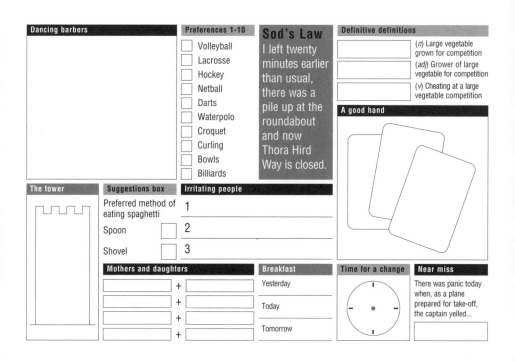

Dancing barbers

Preferences 1-10

- [ ] Volleyball
- [ ] Lacrosse
- [ ] Hockey
- [ ] Netball
- [ ] Darts
- [ ] Waterpolo
- [ ] Croquet
- [ ] Curling
- [ ] Bowls
- [ ] Billiards

Sod's Law

I left twenty minutes earlier than usual, there was a pile up at the roundabout and now Thora Hird Way is closed.

Definitive definitions

(*n*) Large vegetable grown for competition

(*adj*) Grower of large vegetable for competition

(*v*) Cheating at a large vegetable competition

A good hand

The tower

Suggestions box

Preferred method of eating spaghetti

Spoon [ ]

Shovel [ ]

Irritating people

1

2

3

Mothers and daughters

[ ] + [ ]
[ ] + [ ]
[ ] + [ ]
[ ] + [ ]

Breakfast

Yesterday

Today

Tomorrow

Time for a change

Near miss

There was panic today when, as a plane prepared for take-off, the captain yelled...

You find a monkey
knocking on the door

Let him in ☐

Ask him to shave ☐

1 _____

2 _____

3 _____

Dead

Cruise

Safety

☐ Cockroaches
☐ Hares
☐ Kangaroos
☐ Locusts
☐ Parrots
☐ Rats
☐ Squirrels
☐ Turtles
☐ Whales
☐ Wolves

Occurrences

There was
another case
of mistaken
identity, a
child delivered
the papers
and after
some daylight
it got dark.

Everybody in the large
crowd was stunned
and amazed when the
magician removed his...

Busy, busy   Antisocial

Dead superstars who
are even more famous

Hanky Panky

Mon   Tues   Wed   Thurs   Fri

| The last bowl | Rhymes of crime | The Minister's address | Graffiti wall |

The last bowl

The Ditch ●

The Mat ☐

Aren't they marvellous?
They arrive to fix your damp proofing and depart leaving a huge bill and a major subsidence problem.

Rhymes of crime

Thief

Stealing

Fraud

The Minister's address

The Minister...
....
....
....
Heckler..

The Cartwrights

Vital questions

How did you manage to ☐

Is it possible to ☐

Where did you get ☐

Who spilled the ☐

Marks out of 10

Express ☐
Telegraph ☐
Sport ☐
Guardian ☐
Star ☐
Mail ☐
Times ☐
Mirror ☐
Independent ☐
Sun ☐

Nice figure

Graffiti wall

Consensus

It is here today but gone tomorrow

Agree ☐

Disagree ☐

Worth doing

Stand in front of a mirror, stare at your reflection then turn your head gradually to the right, maintaining eye contact. Repeat to the left.

All red or all read

1 _____
2 _____
3 _____

It's official!

In order to make the day pass more pleasantly it has been decreed that the Actress of the Day is...

Floral tribute

Special delivery

Marks out of 10

Base Toadstool ☐
Blusher ☐
Chanterelle ☐
Death Cap ☐
Honey Fungus ☐
Morel ☐
Purple Blewit ☐
Shaggy Ink Cap ☐
Stinkhorn ☐
Yellow Stainer ☐

I am a mole and I live in a hole

Desires - A nip and tuck

On the podium

Word association

Mean

Cider

Idyllic

Multi-tasking

After being enthused by Changing Rooms create a copy of the Venus De Milo and The Kiss to fit in your front room.

Poor performers

Things that don't do what they are supposed to

Chinese meals

1
2
3

Dilemmas

Watching horror movies in the dark

It's the only way ☐

Who said that? ☐

The void

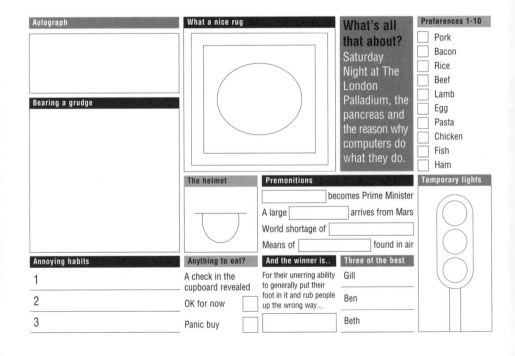

Autograph

Bearing a grudge

Annoying habits

1 _____

2 _____

3 _____

What a nice rug

The helmet

Anything to eat?

A check in the
cupboard revealed

OK for now ☐

Panic buy ☐

What's all that about?

Saturday Night at The London Palladium, the pancreas and the reason why computers do what they do.

Premonitions

[   ] becomes Prime Minister

A large [   ] arrives from Mars

World shortage of [   ]

Means of [   ] found in air

And the winner is..

For their unerring ability to generally put their foot in it and rub people up the wrong way...

Three of the best

Gill

Ben

Beth

Preferences 1-10

☐ Pork
☐ Bacon
☐ Rice
☐ Beef
☐ Lamb
☐ Egg
☐ Pasta
☐ Chicken
☐ Fish
☐ Ham

Temporary lights

Star turns	Dilemmas	Pleasant people	Special K	Poles apart

Star turns
Penelope

Frederick

Kate

Dilemmas
Whether to enjoy the team building day

Let's go ☐

Let's not ☐

Pleasant people
1

2

3

Special K
K

Poles apart
Stores not to be visited to do the shopping

The void	Great events in history		Flying circus

Thought for the day

Actions speak louder than words unless you shout much louder and use a megaphone at the same time.

Preferences 1-10

☐ Drew Barrymore
☐ Jim Carrey
☐ Cyd Charisse
☐ Gary Cooper
☐ Grace Kelly
☐ Paul Newman
☐ Michelle Pfeiffer
☐ Ronald Reagan
☐ Omar Sharif
☐ Natalie Wood

Join the dots

Price fixing - I bought the building

Date

Pay

The Sum of   £

1345 673 2759 02

Bad behaviour
There was near total panic at the zoo today when the gibbons escaped and started to...

Bonfire night

To be considered

Just one more tiny mouthful?

Oh, go on then ☐

Got a sickbag? ☐

Recycling

Collect several sheets and ask friends round for an origami evening making paper planes, party hats and items of interesting jewellery.

Personal ads

Classifieds

_____

_____

_____

_____

Shocked face

Was this really thought through?

1 _____

2 _____

3 _____

It's only V words

V _____

V _____

V _____

Gross untruths

[ ] can support 3.5 tonnes

[ ] helps relieve arthritis

[ ] is red

[ ] is quite a nice person

Concentration levels

What was that?

10.00 11.00 12.00 13.00 14.00 15.00 16.00

Just saying

I wouldn't have done it that way if I were you, it takes twice as long as my way, which is not as long and half as good.

Development land

Marks out of 10

Rain ☐
Windy ☐
Sunny ☐
Drizzle ☐
Hail ☐
Cloudy ☐
Snow ☐
Mild ☐
Thunder ☐
Cool ☐

Portrait gallery - Lady Penelope

Opposites

Hot

Young

Negative

Marks out of 10

Baroque ☐
Cubism ☐
Surrealism ☐
Mannerism ☐
Pop Art ☐
Primitivism ☐
Realism ☐
Fauvism ☐
Romanticism ☐
Rococo ☐

Options

Places to dump a body, just in case you have to

Certifiable

Awarded to

for their

Signed

The truth hurts - Overdressing

....
....
....

Charities

1

2

3

Table Mountain

Rubber stamp

It had been decided that skirts and shorts should no longer be more than six inches above the...

The void

Dilemmas

Which religion to join for the week

Mormons ☐

Normans ☐

Finish it off

Perfect timing

Just as the yacht race was just about to get underway somebody turned up with a flag and a claxon.

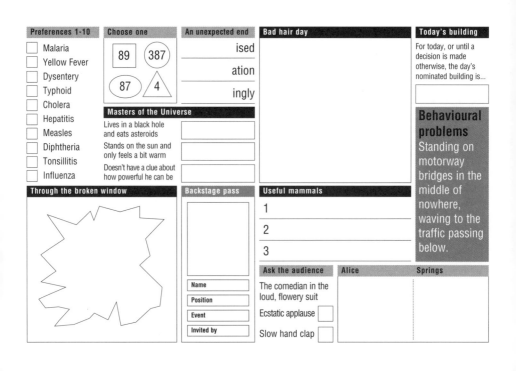

Preferences 1-10
- Malaria
- Yellow Fever
- Dysentery
- Typhoid
- Cholera
- Hepatitis
- Measles
- Diphtheria
- Tonsillitis
- Influenza

Choose one

89 387

87 4

An unexpected end

ised

ation

ingly

Masters of the Universe

Lives in a black hole and eats asteroids

Stands on the sun and only feels a bit warm

Doesn't have a clue about how powerful he can be

Bad hair day

Today's building

For today, or until a decision is made otherwise, the day's nominated building is...

Behavioural problems

Standing on motorway bridges in the middle of nowhere, waving to the traffic passing below.

Through the broken window

Backstage pass

Name

Position

Event

Invited by

Useful mammals

1

2

3

Ask the audience

The comedian in the loud, flowery suit

Ecstatic applause

Slow hand clap

Alice

Springs

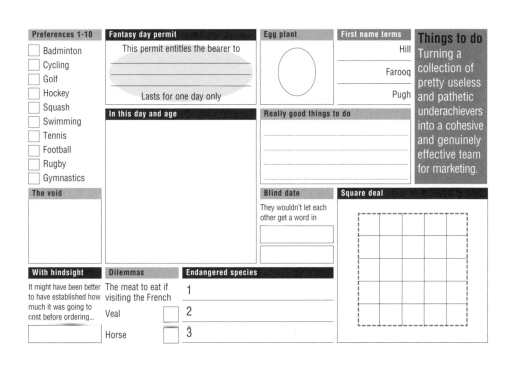

Preferences 1-10
- [ ] Badminton
- [ ] Cycling
- [ ] Golf
- [ ] Hockey
- [ ] Squash
- [ ] Swimming
- [ ] Tennis
- [ ] Football
- [ ] Rugby
- [ ] Gymnastics

The void

Fantasy day permit
This permit entitles the bearer to

Lasts for one day only

In this day and age

With hindsight
It might have been better to have established how much it was going to cost before ordering...

Dilemmas
The meat to eat if visiting the French

Veal

Horse

Endangered species
1
2
3

Egg plant

Really good things to do

Blind date
They wouldn't let each other get a word in

Square deal

First name terms
Hill

Farooq

Pugh

Things to do
Turning a collection of pretty useless and pathetic underachievers into a cohesive and genuinely effective team for marketing.

Definitive definitions

☐ (*n*) Deposits found behind the fridge

☐ (*adj*) A lottery ticket with two matching numbers

☐ (*v*) Biting a chilli when expecting a green bean

Is this a repeat?

Sod's Law

I'd rather have gone down the pub, there's an odd smell in the cinema and now Mr Rustling has sat behind me.

Possessions

Fountain Pen ☐
Blue Soap ☐
Holdall ☐
Stopwatch ☐
Bicycle Pump ☐
Flip-flops ☐
Barbecue ☐
Filofax ☐
Stamp Collection ☐
Athena Poster ☐

Fire!

Forbidden fruit

1 _____

2 _____

3 _____

The verdict

Picking at scabs until they become infected ☐

Guilty ☐

Not guilty ☐

Gold medal

You what!?

You're going to set off in a fleet of small, wooden boats to chart a hitherto undiscovered continent and prove that the earth isn't flat.

Petrol logo

Working hours

Yesterday _____

Today _____

Tomorrow _____

The necessary ingredients

☐ + ☐ = ☐

☐ + ☐ = ☐

☐ + ☐ = ☐

Your name in lights

Hate mail

_____

_____

_____

First thought

Tent

Bounce

Grip

Certificate

Awarded to

_____

for their

_____

_____

Signed

Preferences 1-10

- [ ] Devon
- [ ] Fife
- [ ] Norfolk
- [ ] Powys
- [ ] Surrey
- [ ] Yorkshire
- [ ] Kent
- [ ] Derbyshire
- [ ] Cornwall
- [ ] Essex

At the next roundabout

Stock-taking

The right time to take stock

4.30pm

1.45am

Tonight Matthew...

I'm going to expose most of my body to divert attention from the fact that I can't sing, and be...

Aren't they marvellous?

You vote them in and they spend five years moving goalposts, re-writing history and smiling for the cameras.

Fish out of water

1 _____

2 _____

3 _____

Beaver

Amazing stunts

Daring Denzil dives _____

Squirrelman jumps over _____

Rocketman _____ on his bike

The Loonster falls _____

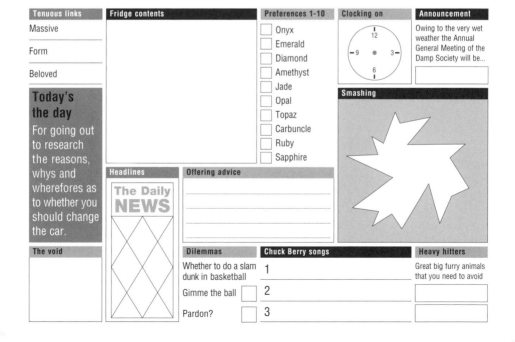

Tenuous links

Massive

Form

Beloved

Today's the day

For going out to research the reasons, whys and wherefores as to whether you should change the car.

The void

Fridge contents

Headlines

The Daily
NEWS

Preferences 1-10

☐ Onyx
☐ Emerald
☐ Diamond
☐ Amethyst
☐ Jade
☐ Opal
☐ Topaz
☐ Carbuncle
☐ Ruby
☐ Sapphire

Offering advice

Dilemmas

Whether to do a slam dunk in basketball

Gimme the ball

Pardon?

Clocking on

12
9 3
6

Smashing

Chuck Berry songs

1

2

3

Announcement

Owing to the very wet weather the Annual General Meeting of the Damp Society will be...

Heavy hitters

Great big furry animals that you need to avoid

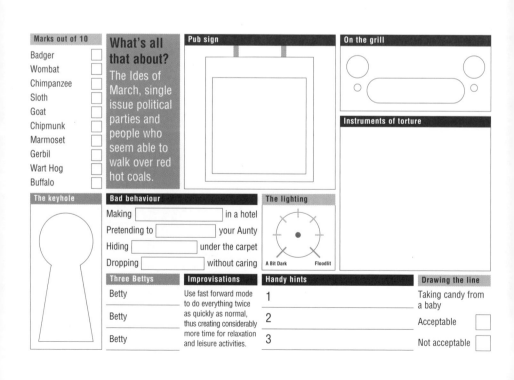

Marks out of 10

- Badger ☐
- Wombat ☐
- Chimpanzee ☐
- Sloth ☐
- Goat ☐
- Chipmunk ☐
- Marmoset ☐
- Gerbil ☐
- Wart Hog ☐
- Buffalo ☐

What's all that about?

The Ides of March, single issue political parties and people who seem able to walk over red hot coals.

Pub sign

On the grill

Instruments of torture

The keyhole

Bad behaviour

Making [ ] in a hotel

Pretending to [ ] your Aunty

Hiding [ ] under the carpet

Dropping [ ] without caring

The lighting

A Bit Dark — Floodlit

Three Bettys

Betty

Betty

Betty

Improvisations

Use fast forward mode to do everything twice as quickly as normal, thus creating considerably more time for relaxation and leisure activities.

Handy hints

1

2

3

Drawing the line

Taking candy from a baby

Acceptable ☐

Not acceptable ☐

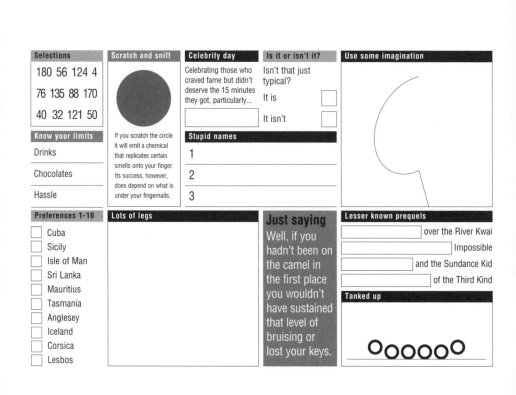

Selections

180 56 124 4

76 135 88 170

40 32 121 50

Know your limits

Drinks

Chocolates

Hassle

Scratch and sniff

If you scratch the circle it will emit a chemical that replicates certain smells onto your finger. Its success, however, does depend on what is under your fingernails.

Celebrity day

Celebrating those who craved fame but didn't deserve the 15 minutes they got, particularly...

Stupid names

1

2

3

Is it or isn't it?

Isn't that just typical?

It is

It isn't

Use some imagination

Preferences 1-10

Cuba

Sicily

Isle of Man

Sri Lanka

Mauritius

Tasmania

Anglesey

Iceland

Corsica

Lesbos

Lots of legs

Just saying

Well, if you hadn't been on the camel in the first place you wouldn't have sustained that level of bruising or lost your keys.

Lesser known prequels

over the River Kwai

Impossible

and the Sundance Kid

of the Third Kind

Tanked up

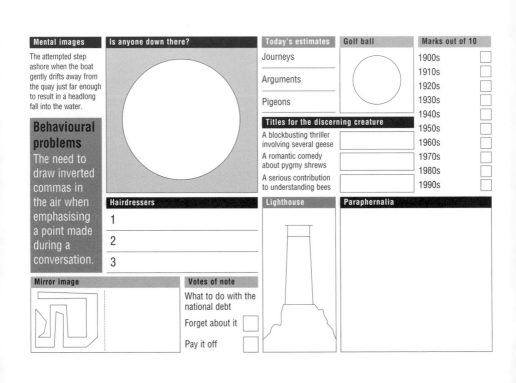

Mental images

The attempted step ashore when the boat gently drifts away from the quay just far enough to result in a headlong fall into the water.

Behavioural problems

The need to draw inverted commas in the air when emphasising a point made during a conversation.

Mirror image

Is anyone down there?

Hairdressers

1

2

3

Votes of note

What to do with the national debt

Forget about it

Pay it off

Today's estimates

Journeys

Arguments

Pigeons

Titles for the discerning creature

A blockbusting thriller involving several geese

A romantic comedy about pygmy shrews

A serious contribution to understanding bees

Golf ball

Lighthouse

Marks out of 10

1900s

1910s

1920s

1930s

1940s

1950s

1960s

1970s

1980s

1990s

Paraphernalia

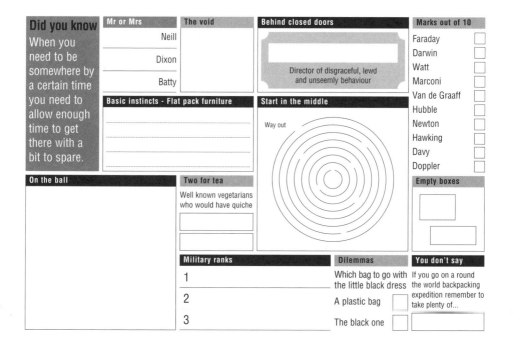

Did you know When you need to be somewhere by a certain time you need to allow enough time to get there with a bit to spare.

Mr or Mrs
Neill
Dixon
Batty

The void

Behind closed doors
Director of disgraceful, lewd and unseemly behaviour

Marks out of 10
Faraday ☐
Darwin ☐
Watt ☐
Marconi ☐
Van de Graaff ☐
Hubble ☐
Newton ☐
Hawking ☐
Davy ☐
Doppler ☐

Basic instincts - Flat pack furniture

On the ball

Start in the middle
Way out

Two for tea
Well known vegetarians who would have quiche

Empty boxes

Military ranks
1
2
3

Dilemmas
Which bag to go with the little black dress
A plastic bag ☐
The black one ☐

You don't say
If you go on a round the world backpacking expedition remember to take plenty of...

Cheese & Pickle
Salmon
Chicken Salad
Prawn & Mayo
Ham Salad
BLT
Ham & Cheese
Chicken Korma
Cucumber
Tuna & Mayo

Sod's Law

The pack contained instructions in Italian only, assembly needed a small warehouse and half the bits were missing.

(adj) Skin colouring after a heavy night

(n) A male who dresses to the right

(v) Attempting to calm an over-friendly pet

Preferred method of motivating colleagues

Slap on the head

Molly-coddling

1
2
3

V
V
V
V

Yesterday

Today

Tomorrow

The nation was shocked today when, during the Queen's speech, a footman decided to...

Dilemmas	The void	Wet blankets		Bedroom activities

Dilemmas

Which pair of trainers to wear today

The trained ones ☐

The wild ones ☐

The void

Wet blankets

1 _____

2 _____

3 _____

Bedroom activities

The Door

The Bed

The Wardrobe

The Window

The first half

Department

Holly

Basket

Point of impact

Preferences 1-10

☐ Greenland
☐ Borneo
☐ Baffin
☐ Honshu
☐ Java
☐ Cuba
☐ Iceland
☐ Ireland
☐ Hokkaido
☐ Hispaniola

Occurrences

It was very fashionable for men to wear powdered wigs, it was difficult to fly and eating some things rotted teeth.

An embarrassing moment

The big deal

If Sir Elton John called by and offered to play one of his songs the obvious choice is...

Apathy gauge

Maybe   Who cares

Doublers

Impressive, snow peaked mountain ranges

The ins and the outs

In —————————

———————— Out

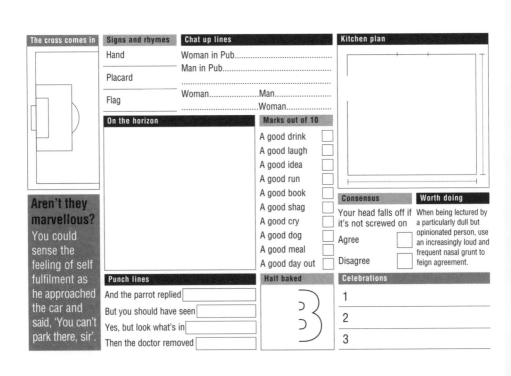

The cross comes in

Signs and rhymes

Hand

Placard

Flag

Chat up lines

Woman in Pub...

Man in Pub...

....

Woman...................Man..............................

...................................Woman...................

Kitchen plan

On the horizon

Marks out of 10

A good drink ☐

A good laugh ☐

A good idea ☐

A good run ☐

A good book ☐

A good shag ☐

A good cry ☐

A good dog ☐

A good meal ☐

A good day out ☐

Aren't they marvellous?

You could sense the feeling of self fulfilment as he approached the car and said, 'You can't park there, sir'.

Consensus

Your head falls off if it's not screwed on

Agree ☐

Disagree ☐

Worth doing

When being lectured by a particularly dull but opinionated person, use an increasingly loud and frequent nasal grunt to feign agreement.

Punch lines

And the parrot replied [ ]

But you should have seen [ ]

Yes, but look what's in [ ]

Then the doctor removed [ ]

Half baked

Ʒ

Celebrations

1 _____

2 _____

3 _____

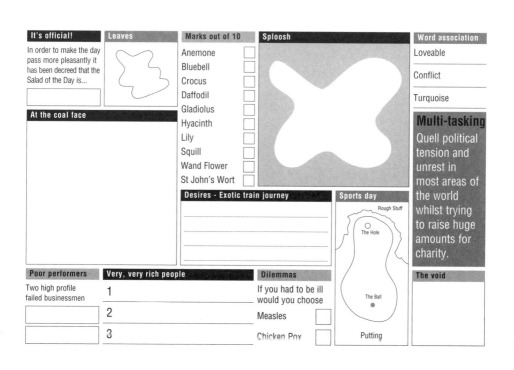

It's official!

In order to make the day pass more pleasantly it has been decreed that the Salad of the Day is...

At the coal face

Poor performers

Two high profile failed businessmen

Leaves

Marks out of 10

Anemone ☐
Bluebell ☐
Crocus ☐
Daffodil ☐
Gladiolus ☐
Hyacinth ☐
Lily ☐
Squill ☐
Wand Flower ☐
St John's Wort ☐

Desires - Exotic train journey

Very, very rich people

1
2
3

Sploosh

Dilemmas

If you had to be ill would you choose

Measles ☐

Chicken Pox ☐

Sports day

Rough Stuff

The Hole

The Ball

Putting

Word association

Loveable

Conflict

Turquoise

Multi-tasking

Quell political tension and unrest in most areas of the world whilst trying to raise huge amounts for charity.

The void

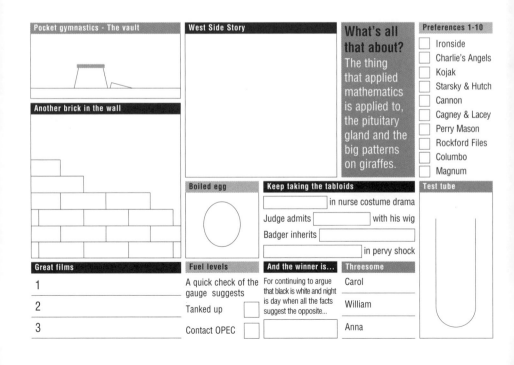

Pocket gymnastics - The vault

Another brick in the wall

Great films

1

2

3

West Side Story

Boiled egg

Fuel levels

A quick check of the gauge suggests

Tanked up

Contact OPEC

And the winner is...

For continuing to argue that black is white and night is day when all the facts suggest the opposite...

Keep taking the tabloids

in nurse costume drama

Judge admits with his wig

Badger inherits

in pervy shock

Threesome

Carol

William

Anna

What's all that about?
The thing that applied mathematics is applied to, the pituitary gland and the big patterns on giraffes.

Preferences 1-10

Ironside
Charlie's Angels
Kojak
Starsky & Hutch
Cannon
Cagney & Lacey
Perry Mason
Rockford Files
Columbo
Magnum

Test tube

Darren

Valerie

Lennox

What to do if you
lose your job

Panic ☐

Celebrate ☐

1

2

3

T

A very kindly old gent
and a complete git

Thought for the day

It is highly
unlikely that
anybody could
be stupid
enough to
throw the
baby out with
the bathwater.

☐ Robert Palmer
☐ Small Faces
☐ Pet Shop Boys
☐ Marc Almond
☐ Mariah Carey
☐ Nina Simone
☐ Whitesnake
☐ Chas and Dave
☐ Luther Vandross
☐ Michael Jackson

☐ − ☐ − ☐ − ☐ = ☐

☐ + ☐ + ☐ + ☐ = ☐

☐ − ☐ − ☐ − ☐ = ☐

There was mayhem at
the launch of a new
range of underwear when
one of the models...

Still life

To be considered

Running naked out of a shop's fitting room

No chance ☐

For a dare ☐

Recycling

When completed put this sheet in a safe place ready to use as Christmas wrapping paper for a small but expensive present.

Main courses

1 _____

2 _____

3 _____

Notice board

The Big
EVENT

Baby face

It's only C words

C _____

C _____

C _____

Patent pending

_____ to remove earwax

_____ to clear up after babies

_____ to catch a falling star

_____ to wipe out the rainforests

Projected overtime

Extra bunce

Mon Tues Wed Thurs Fri Sat Sun

Just saying

When I was young you could get two gallons of petrol, three pints of bitter and still have change from a pound note.

Up the creek

Marks out of 10

Wellingtons ☐

Sandals ☐

Lace-ups ☐

Clogs ☐

Trainers ☐

Slip-ons ☐

Brogues ☐

Flip-flops ☐

Hiking Boots ☐

Slippers ☐

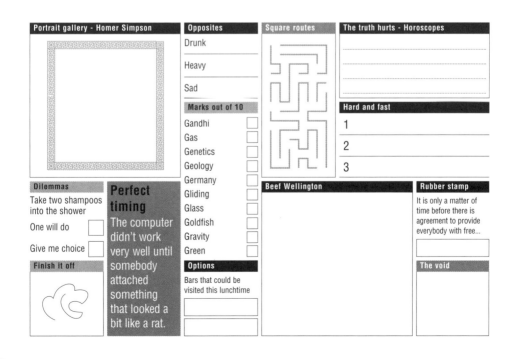

Portrait gallery - Homer Simpson

Opposites

Drunk

Heavy

Sad

Square routes

The truth hurts - Horoscopes

Marks out of 10

Gandhi

Gas

Genetics

Geology

Germany

Gliding

Glass

Goldfish

Gravity

Green

Hard and fast

1

2

3

Dilemmas

Take two shampoos into the shower

One will do

Give me choice

Finish it off

Perfect timing

The computer didn't work very well until somebody attached something that looked a bit like a rat.

Options

Bars that could be visited this lunchtime

Beef Wellington

Rubber stamp

It is only a matter of time before there is agreement to provide everybody with free...

The void

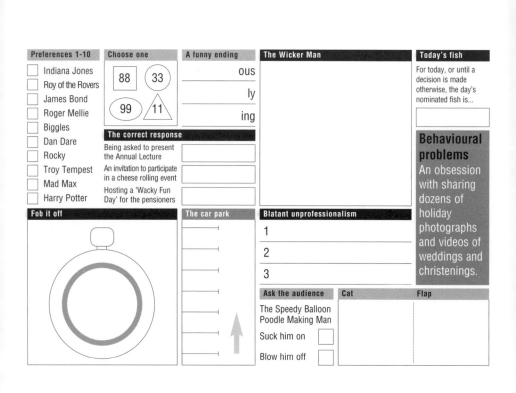

Preferences 1-10
- Indiana Jones
- Roy of the Rovers
- James Bond
- Roger Mellie
- Biggles
- Dan Dare
- Rocky
- Troy Tempest
- Mad Max
- Harry Potter

Choose one

88　33
99　11

A funny ending

ous

ly

ing

The Wicker Man

Today's fish

For today, or until a decision is made otherwise, the day's nominated fish is...

Behavioural problems

An obsession with sharing dozens of holiday photographs and videos of weddings and christenings.

The correct response

Being asked to present the Annual Lecture

An invitation to participate in a cheese rolling event

Hosting a 'Wacky Fun Day' for the pensioners

Fob it off

The car park

Blatant unprofessionalism

1

2

3

Ask the audience

The Speedy Balloon Poodle Making Man

Suck him on

Blow him off

Cat

Flap

Preferences 1-10

- Malaysia
- France
- Congo
- Mozambique
- Latvia
- Austria
- Scotland
- Pakistan
- Guatemala
- Colombia

The void

Tickets please

Admit One

Gold Club Member   8734 2784 9071 5282

Gargoyles!

Having a ball

First name terms

Gold

Lloyd

Simpson

Really good things to do

Things to do

Putting what is good for you, and you only, at the top of the agenda for once without other things spoiling it.

Blind date

The complete cad and the English rose

Pixelated image

With hindsight

It might well have been far better not to have handed the button for a nuclear holocaust to...

Dilemmas

Taking up dance classes to get down

Line dancing

Discomania

Tree fellers

1

2

3

Definitive definitions

☐	(*n*) The particularly anxious traveller
☐	(*adj*) An impressively large and loud firework
☐	(*v*) Eating hand-held food as it disintegrates

After the watershed

Sod's Law

It was the best car I could get for the money, apparently it had always made that noise, and now I know why.

Possessions

Plastic Mac ☐
Birthmark ☐
Road Atlas ☐
Some Francs ☐
Tattoo ☐
Clothes Horse ☐
Sports Trophy ☐
Pack of Cards ☐
Big Peppermill ☐
A Sea Shell ☐

The Sun has got his hat on

Blue things (or purple)

1 _____

2 _____

3 _____

The verdict

Starting a prank that went horribly wrong

Guilty ☐

Not guilty ☐

In the wardrobe

You what!?

Despite acquiring massive debts, I'm going to close my company down, ignore the creditors and start up under a brand new name.

Charity logo

Biggest worry

Yesterday _____

Today _____

Tomorrow _____

Sum things to do

☐ + ☐ + ☐ + ☐ = ☐

☐ − ☐ − ☐ − ☐ = ☐

☐ + ☐ + ☐ + ☐ = ☐

The paparazzi strike again

Prominent Swedes

1 _____

2 _____

3 _____

The void

Dilemmas

Which Soap to watch later on

Eastenders ☐

Coronation St ☐

Marks out of 10

Major ☐
Callaghan ☐
Churchill ☐
Blair ☐
Heath ☐
Wilson ☐
Chamberlain ☐
Lloyd-George ☐
Thatcher ☐
MacMillan ☐

Opening the floodgates

The second half

Gas
_____
Business
_____
Room

Half and half

Thinking ahead

When you are preparing for a camping expedition make sure you take a tent, a sleeping bag and a...

Essential activities

This Morning

This Afternoon

This Evening

Pairing up

Something expensive and something cheap

Celebrations - Losing your virginity

What a total waste of time

Sitting in a stationary tailback on the M6, M4 or whatever and getting really worked up about it.

Skinny dipping

Bounced cheque

Date

Pay

The Sum of   £

1345 673 2759 02

First thought

Speed

Hot

Mud

Skydiving

Geography trip

Studying interesting land formations

South America

South Shields

Tonight Matthew...

I'm going to put my hand up a dummy's backside, hope that you don't notice my lips moving, and be...

Preferences 1-10

Cliff

Plateau

Gorge

Mountain

Slope

Hill

Plain

Valley

Ridge

Glen

Welcome

Welcome to

Please drive

Aren't they marvellous?

You place your food order as soon as you arrive, but it turns up cold just before you have to return to work.

Planets to visit

1

2

3

Bear faced cheek

Disasters

It was OK before

The dog's eaten

I didn't see   until it was too late

Another 2.5 seconds and

Quick

Discreet

Exciting

Today's the day

For vainly hoping that some distant but very rich relative leaves you a huge fortune in their will.

The void

Basking sharks

Headlines

The Daily NEWS

Preferences 1-10

☐ Steel
☐ Linen
☐ Lace
☐ Ivory
☐ Crystal
☐ Silver
☐ Pearl
☐ Ruby
☐ Gold
☐ Diamond

Offering advice

Dilemmas

Which hairpiece to put on to impress

The Ginger one ☐

The Curly one ☐

Full time

12
9 • 3
6

Four sisters

Little niggles

1

2

3

Announcement

It is with deep regret that we have to say that from now on there will no longer be any...

Heavy hitters

Impressive big name radio personalities

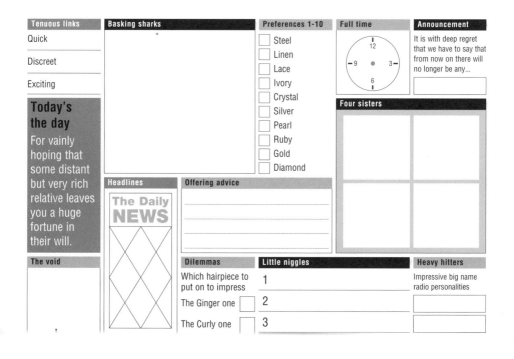

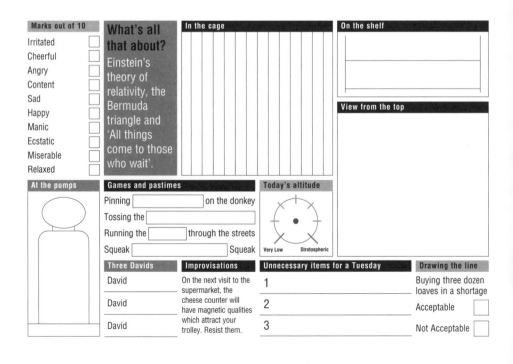

Marks out of 10		What's all that about?
Irritated	☐	Einstein's theory of relativity, the Bermuda triangle and 'All things come to those who wait'.
Cheerful	☐	
Angry	☐	
Content	☐	
Sad	☐	
Happy	☐	
Manic	☐	
Ecstatic	☐	
Miserable	☐	
Relaxed	☐	

In the cage

On the shelf

View from the top

At the pumps

Games and pastimes

Pinning [ ] on the donkey

Tossing the [ ]

Running the [ ] through the streets

Squeak [ ] Squeak

Today's altitude

Very Low   Stratospheric

Three Davids

David

David

David

Improvisations

On the next visit to the supermarket, the cheese counter will have magnetic qualities which attract your trolley. Resist them.

Unnecessary items for a Tuesday

1

2

3

Drawing the line

Buying three dozen loaves in a shortage

Acceptable ☐

Not Acceptable ☐

Great figures	Epic encounters	BBC comedies		Best mates	Dilemmas

Great figures

-88
+7

Epic encounters

Finalists in the dour
Scotsman competition

BBC comedies

1
2
3

Best mates

Chandler

Isobel

Ken

Dilemmas

What to build
before going home

A bridge ☐

A cathedral ☐

A bath of beans

It really could happen

Weddings involving large but fragmented families will pass peacefully without tears, screaming or fighting.

Holding forth - Amateur experts

Down in the depths

Marks out of 10

Kiwi ☐
Bald Eagle ☐
Chaffinch ☐
Dipper ☐
Robin ☐
Tit ☐
Wagtail ☐
Loon ☐
Shag ☐
Puffin ☐

Over-reactions

It may well not have been a penalty but that was no reason to go up to the referee and say...

Important labelling

Dangerous Cargo

The void

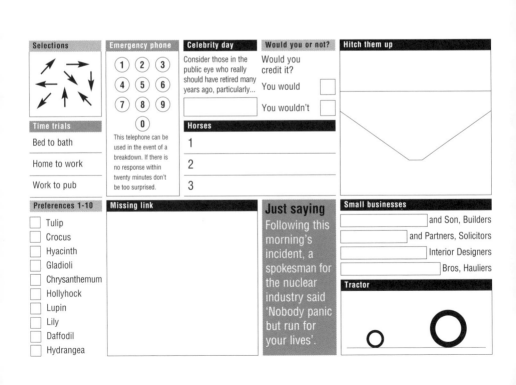

Selections

Time trials

Bed to bath

Home to work

Work to pub

Preferences 1-10

- [ ] Tulip
- [ ] Crocus
- [ ] Hyacinth
- [ ] Gladioli
- [ ] Chrysanthemum
- [ ] Hollyhock
- [ ] Lupin
- [ ] Lily
- [ ] Daffodil
- [ ] Hydrangea

Emergency phone

(1) (2) (3)
(4) (5) (6)
(7) (8) (9)
(0)

This telephone can be used in the event of a breakdown. If there is no response within twenty minutes don't be too surprised.

Missing link

Celebrity day

Consider those in the public eye who really should have retired many years ago, particularly...

Horses

1

2

3

Would you or not?

Would you credit it?

You would [ ]

You wouldn't [ ]

Just saying

Following this morning's incident, a spokesman for the nuclear industry said 'Nobody panic but run for your lives'.

Hitch them up

Small businesses

[_____] and Son, Builders

[_____] and Partners, Solicitors

[_____] Interior Designers

[_____] Bros, Hauliers

Tractor

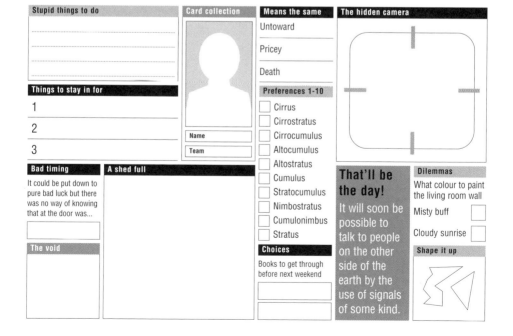

Stupid things to do

Things to stay in for

1

2

3

Bad timing

It could be put down to pure bad luck but there was no way of knowing that at the door was...

The void

A shed full

Card collection

Name

Team

Means the same

Untoward

Pricey

Death

Preferences 1-10

☐ Cirrus
☐ Cirrostratus
☐ Cirrocumulus
☐ Altocumulus
☐ Altostratus
☐ Cumulus
☐ Stratocumulus
☐ Nimbostratus
☐ Cumulonimbus
☐ Stratus

Choices

Books to get through before next weekend

The hidden camera

That'll be the day!

It will soon be possible to talk to people on the other side of the earth by the use of signals of some kind.

Dilemmas

What colour to paint the living room wall

Misty buff ☐

Cloudy sunrise ☐

Shape it up

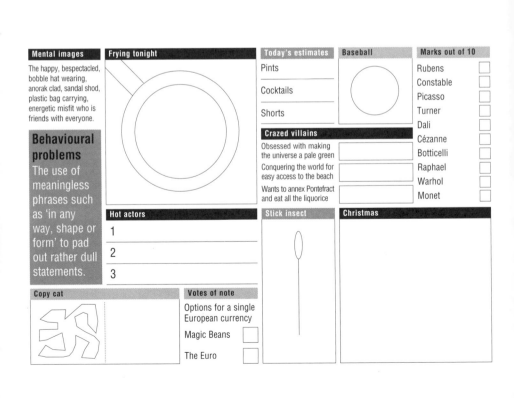

Mental images

The happy, bespectacled, bobble hat wearing, anorak clad, sandal shod, plastic bag carrying, energetic misfit who is friends with everyone.

Behavioural problems

The use of meaningless phrases such as 'in any way, shape or form' to pad out rather dull statements.

Frying tonight

Hot actors

1

2

3

Copy cat

Today's estimates

Pints

Cocktails

Shorts

Crazed villains

Obsessed with making the universe a pale green

Conquering the world for easy access to the beach

Wants to annex Pontefract and eat all the liquorice

Stick insect

Votes of note

Options for a single European currency

Magic Beans

The Euro

Baseball

Marks out of 10

Rubens

Constable

Picasso

Turner

Dali

Cézanne

Botticelli

Raphael

Warhol

Monet

Christmas

Did you know

In ancient Rome things were not considered ancient but pretty much up to date and cutting edge for the time.

Mr or Mrs

Donovan

Price

Gregory

Basic instincts - Football hooligans

I don't like Mondays

The void

Two for tea

Rock Gods to pop in for a light supper

Private plate

Pen darts

1 2 3 4 5 7 9 **10** 9 7 5 4 3 2 1

Petrol companies

1

2

3

Dilemmas

Which vegetables to grow in the garden

Carrots

Cabbages

Marks out of 10

Battery

Carbon Fibre

Credit Card

Light Bulb

Hovercraft

Match

Parachute

Radar

Stapler

Windmill

Empty boxes

You don't say

When turning up at the Palace to be presented with your gong do not be rude and say...

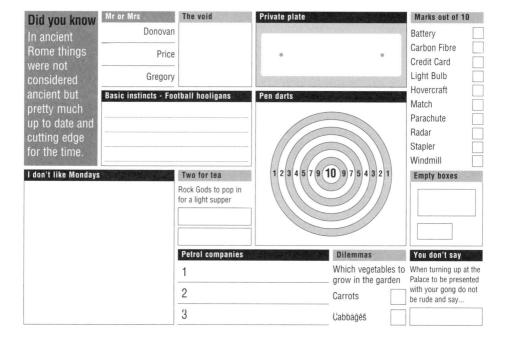

Spaghetti Junction

Preferences 1-10
- [ ] Geography
- [ ] Physics
- [ ] German
- [ ] Maths
- [ ] History
- [ ] Biology
- [ ] PE
- [ ] French
- [ ] Chemistry
- [ ] Art

Sod's Law

I'd bought a new suit, learnt the entire history of the company but the job went to the jerk with the long neck.

Definitive definitions

	(adj) A jigsaw with one piece missing
	(n) The stuff that sticks to velcro fastenings
	(v) Handling something very hot without gloves

Measles or chicken pox

Cliff walking

Suggestions box

A better use for Greenland

A cool box [ ]

A huge sled run [ ]

The absolute dregs

1 _____

2 _____

3 _____

Interesting cocktails

	+	
	+	
	+	
	+	

Eating out

Yesterday _____

Today _____

Tomorrow _____

The next time

12
9   3
6

No mates

Fighting broke out between the contestants at the World Chess Final when the adjudicator...

Daily dilemma	The void	Beatles hits		The route to work

Daily dilemma

How to celebrate
St David's Day

With a leek ☐

A tall hat ☐

The void

Beatles hits

1

2

3

The route to work

Home

Next
door

The shop

The first half

Service

Hard

Monkey

Three feathers

Preferences 1-10

☐ Oklahoma!
☐ Carousel
☐ Porgy and Bess
☐ Funny Girl
☐ Cabaret
☐ Flashdance
☐ Sister Act
☐ Staying Alive
☐ Grease
☐ Paint Your Wagon

The pub

Work

Occurrences

Some of the
mountains
were covered
in cloud, the
bus was late
for a change
and an old
lady's cat ran
away again.

An embarrassing moment

The big deal

If you were addressing
the United Nations
about uniting nations
your tone would be...

Misery gauge

Simper   Woe, oh woe

Doublers

Places to stick your
used chewing gum

Mirror image

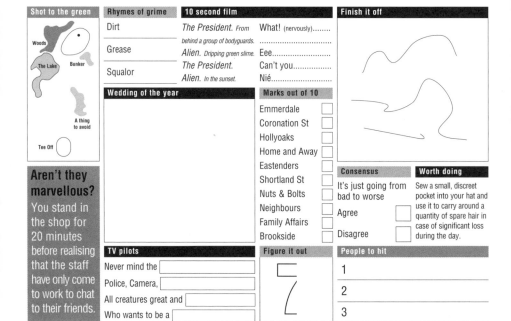

Shot to the green

Woods

The Lake — Bunker

A thing to avoid

Tee Off

Aren't they marvellous?

You stand in the shop for 20 minutes before realising that the staff have only come to work to chat to their friends.

Rhymes of grime

Dirt

Grease

Squalor

Wedding of the year

TV pilots

Never mind the

Police, Camera,

All creatures great and

Who wants to be a

10 second film

The President. From behind a group of bodyguards. What! (nervously)........

Alien. Dripping green slime. Eee.........................

The President. Can't you................

Alien. In the sunset. Nié..........................

Marks out of 10

Emmerdale ☐
Coronation St ☐
Hollyoaks ☐
Home and Away ☐
Eastenders ☐
Shortland St ☐
Nuts & Bolts ☐
Neighbours ☐
Family Affairs ☐
Brookside ☐

Figure it out

Finish it off

Consensus

It's just going from bad to worse

Agree

Disagree ☐

Worth doing

Sew a small, discreet pocket into your hat and use it to carry around a quantity of spare hair in case of significant loss during the day. ☐

People to hit

1

2

3

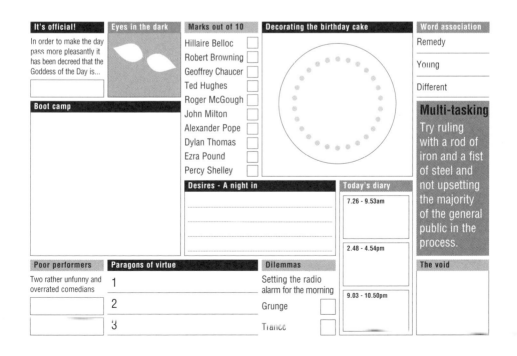

It's official!

In order to make the day pass more pleasantly it has been decreed that the Goddess of the Day is...

Boot camp

Eyes in the dark

Marks out of 10

Hillaire Belloc ☐
Robert Browning ☐
Geoffrey Chaucer ☐
Ted Hughes ☐
Roger McGough ☐
John Milton ☐
Alexander Pope ☐
Dylan Thomas ☐
Ezra Pound ☐
Percy Shelley ☐

Desires - A night in

Decorating the birthday cake

Today's diary

7.26 - 9.53am

2.48 - 4.54pm

9.03 - 10.50pm

Word association

Remedy

Young

Different

Multi-tasking

Try ruling with a rod of iron and a fist of steel and not upsetting the majority of the general public in the process.

Poor performers

Two rather unfunny and overrated comedians

Paragons of virtue

1
2
3

Dilemmas

Setting the radio alarm for the morning

Grunge ☐

Trance ☐

The void

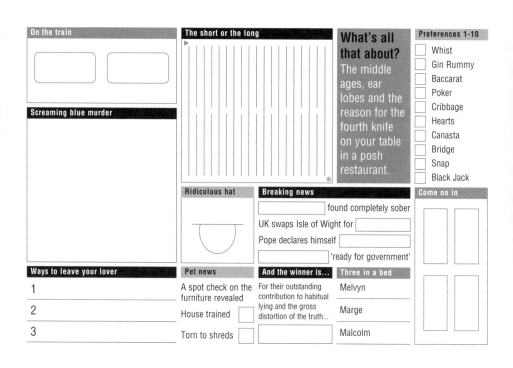

On the train

Screaming blue murder

Ways to leave your lover

1

2

3

The short or the long

Ridiculous hat

Pet news

A spot check on the furniture revealed

House trained

Torn to shreds

What's all that about? The middle ages, ear lobes and the reason for the fourth knife on your table in a posh restaurant.

Breaking news

found completely sober

UK swaps Isle of Wight for

Pope declares himself

'ready for government'

And the winner is...

For their outstanding contribution to habitual lying and the gross distortion of the truth...

Preferences 1-10

Whist
Gin Rummy
Baccarat
Poker
Cribbage
Hearts
Canasta
Bridge
Snap
Black Jack

Come on in

Three in a bed

Melvyn

Marge

Malcolm

Star turns	Dilemmas	Large trees		Join the queue	Poles apart

Star turns

Honey

Simon

Christine

Dilemmas

Deciding to take in a movie tonight

Romantic ☐

All action ☐

Large trees

1 _____

2 _____

3 _____

Join the queue

Q

Poles apart

Things worth having a bit of a fight over

☐

☐

The void

Great events in history

Thought for the day

Beggars can't be choosers unless you give them a random selection of items and ask them to take their pick.

Dream boat

Preferences 1-10

☐ Anne Bancroft
☐ Tom Baker
☐ Richard Burton
☐ Tony Curtis
☐ Marlene Dietrich
☐ Tom Hanks
☐ Sophia Loren
☐ Meg Ryan
☐ Spencer Tracy
☐ Mao Woot

The route from N to B

N

B

Behind you!

Bad behaviour

There was a near panic around the breakfast table when it became clear we'd run out of...

A walk on the wild side

To be considered

Staying in bed for the entire day

Regularly ☐

Only when ill ☐

Recycling

After use, use this page to write your name in big, bold letters. Secure it to your jacket with a safety pin so that others can easily identify you.

Eenin Stanit!

Tonight

Miserable face

Interests to leave out of your CV

1 _____

2 _____

3 _____

It's only Z words

Z _____

Z _____

Z _____

A bit over the top

	to increase income
	to encourage tourists
	to spice up your life
	to reduce wind resistance

Planned creativity

Good Ideas

10.00 11.00 12.00 13.00 14.00 15.00 16.00

Just saying

I realise that swallowing the fly might have been an accident but what she swallowed afterwards was asking for trouble.

Route planner

Marks out of 10

YMCA	☐
VTOL	☐
CAD	☐
AA	☐
VPL	☐
ERNIE	☐
VSO	☐
BBC	☐
HRH	☐
NASA	☐

Down

Wide

Black

Marks out of 10	
Barbados	
Bolivia	
Burundi	
Botswana	
Belgium	
Burkina Faso	
Brazil	
Belarus	
Bulgaria	
Belize	

Favourites menu

Starter

Main Course

Dessert

The truth hurts - Cardigan wearers

Carry-Ons

1

2

3

Dilemmas

Whether to take the umbrella today

Definitely

It won't rain

Finish it off

Perfect timing

Just when the newspaper wondered what to run on the front page it all kicked off with bells on and more.

Options

Which colour tie to wear with the blue shirt

Going out with a bang

Rubber stamp

At the meeting of the Really Bizarre Sports Club it was agreed that the clear winner was...

The void

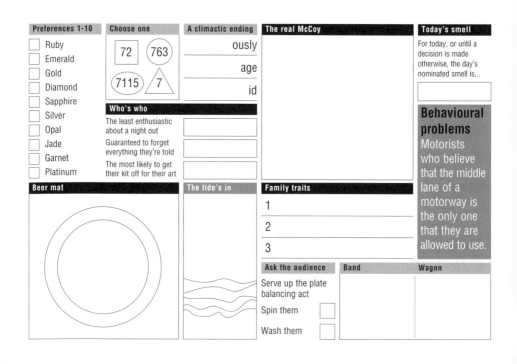

Preferences 1-10

- ☐ Ruby
- ☐ Emerald
- ☐ Gold
- ☐ Diamond
- ☐ Sapphire
- ☐ Silver
- ☐ Opal
- ☐ Jade
- ☐ Garnet
- ☐ Platinum

Choose one

72   763
7115   7

Who's who

The least enthusiastic about a night out

Guaranteed to forget everything they're told

The most likely to get their kit off for their art

Beer mat

A climactic ending

ously

age

id

The tide's in

The real McCoy

Family traits

1

2

3

Ask the audience

Serve up the plate balancing act

Spin them

Wash them

Band

Today's smell

For today, or until a decision is made otherwise, the day's nominated smell is...

Behavioural problems

Motorists who believe that the middle lane of a motorway is the only one that they are allowed to use.

Wagon

Preferences 1-10	Fantasy partner ticket		Round robin	First name terms	**Things to do**

Preferences 1-10

☐ Azalea
☐ Buckthorn
☐ Calico Bush
☐ Forsythia
☐ Heather
☐ Lavender
☐ Peony
☐ Rhododendron
☐ Tiger Lily
☐ Veronica

Fantasy partner ticket

This ticket enables

to go out for the evening with

Piggy in the middle

Round robin

First name terms

Knight

Davies

Walker

Things to do

Ensuring that everyone in the vicinity is aware of your overwhelming desire to succeed at the expense of everything else.

Really good things to do

The void

Blind date

The photographer and the supermodel

Set squares

With hindsight

It might well have been better to have studied the route more carefully before leaving for...

Dilemmas

Which flavour of ice cream to choose

Vanilla ☐

It's still too cold ☐

Chocolate bars

1

2

3

Definitive definitions

☐ (*n*) Noise made by custard as it hits the floor

☐ (*v*) To float like a butterfly and sting like a bee

☐ (*n*) Fundamentalist wing of the politically correct

Children's TV?

Sod's Law

I was dragged into town for 9 o'clock, it took 3 hours to find the right trousers and now we've missed the first half.

Possessions

Toby Jug ☐
Antifreeze ☐
Trainers ☐
Tinsel ☐
Cassette Player ☐
Apron ☐
Shoe Polish ☐
Folding Chair ☐
Jigsaw Puzzle ☐
Hairbrush ☐

The weird whelk

Moral dilemmas

1 _____

2 _____

3 _____

The verdict

Excessive crying over spilt milk

Guilty ☐

Not Guilty ☐

It's in the can

You what!?

So you're going to find a very high bridge, tie one end of a huge elastic rope to it and the other end to your legs, then plummet to the ground.

Airline logo

Love interest

Yesterday _____

Today _____

Tomorrow _____

Number crunching

☐ + ☐ − ☐ x ☐ ÷ ☐ = ☐

☐ ÷ ☐ + ☐ − ☐ x ☐ = ☐

☐ x ☐ ÷ ☐ + ☐ − ☐ = ☐

Holiday snaps

Motor racers

1 _____

2 _____

3 _____

The void

Dilemmas

Which size bra to wear this evening

34B ☐

44GG ☐

Marks out of 10

Peter Blake ☐
Georges Braque ☐
Cézanne ☐
Edgar Degas ☐
Gainsborough ☐
Damien Hurst ☐
William Hogarth ☐
Claude Monet ☐
Jackson Pollock ☐
Van Gogh ☐

The mug tree

The second half

Stock

Pole

Sweep

Half and half

Thinking ahead

When entering the World Downhill Skiing championships it would be good to take...

What a total waste of time

Trying to run before you can walk has always been regarded as futile and is, quite frankly, tricky at best.

Instant favourites

Coffee Shop

Film

Colour

Pairing up

Favourites from the fast food burger takeaway

Celebrations - Winning at Twister

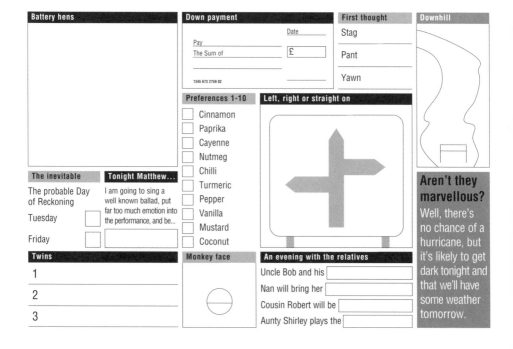

Battery hens

Down payment

Date _____

Pay _____
The Sum of _____   £ _____

1345 673 2759 02   _____

First thought

Stag

Pant

Yawn

Downhill

Preferences 1-10

☐ Cinnamon
☐ Paprika
☐ Cayenne
☐ Nutmeg
☐ Chilli
☐ Turmeric
☐ Pepper
☐ Vanilla
☐ Mustard
☐ Coconut

Left, right or straight on

The inevitable

The probable Day
of Reckoning

Tuesday ☐

Friday ☐

Tonight Matthew...

I am going to sing a
well known ballad, put
far too much emotion into
the performance, and be...

Aren't they marvellous?

Well, there's
no chance of a
hurricane, but
it's likely to get
dark tonight and
that we'll have
some weather
tomorrow.

Twins

1 _____

2 _____

3 _____

Monkey face

An evening with the relatives

Uncle Bob and his _____

Nan will bring her _____

Cousin Robert will be _____

Aunty Shirley plays the _____

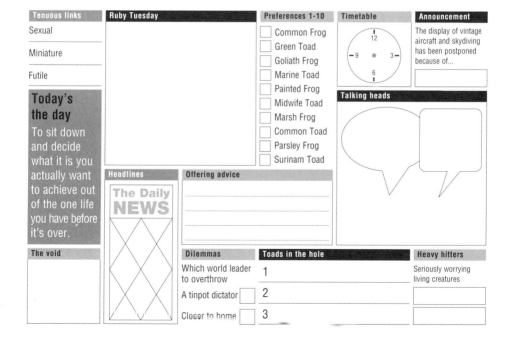

Tenuous links

Sexual

Miniature

Futile

Today's the day

To sit down and decide what it is you actually want to achieve out of the one life you have before it's over.

The void

Ruby Tuesday

Headlines

The Daily NEWS

Preferences 1-10

☐ Common Frog
☐ Green Toad
☐ Goliath Frog
☐ Marine Toad
☐ Painted Frog
☐ Midwife Toad
☐ Marsh Frog
☐ Common Toad
☐ Parsley Frog
☐ Surinam Toad

Offering advice

Dilemmas

Which world leader to overthrow

A tinpot dictator ☐

Closer to home ☐

Timetable

12
9   3
6

Talking heads

Toads in the hole

1

2

3

Announcement

The display of vintage aircraft and skydiving has been postponed because of...

Heavy hitters

Seriously worrying living creatures

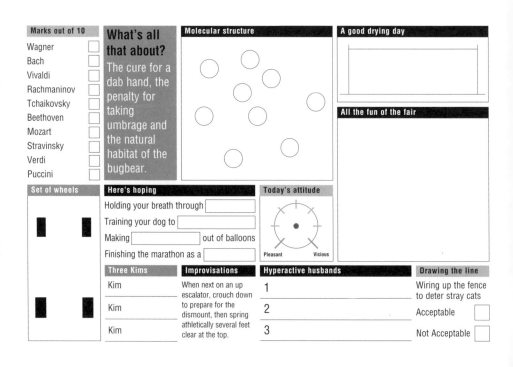

Marks out of 10		What's all that about?
Wagner	☐	The cure for a dab hand, the penalty for taking umbrage and the natural habitat of the bugbear.
Bach	☐	
Vivaldi	☐	
Rachmaninov	☐	
Tchaikovsky	☐	
Beethoven	☐	
Mozart	☐	
Stravinsky	☐	
Verdi	☐	
Puccini	☐	

Molecular structure

A good drying day

All the fun of the fair

Set of wheels

Here's hoping

Holding your breath through ⬚

Training your dog to ⬚

Making ⬚ out of balloons

Finishing the marathon as a ⬚

Today's attitude

Pleasant — Vicious

Three Kims

Kim

Kim

Kim

Improvisations

When next on an up escalator, crouch down to prepare for the dismount, then spring athletically several feet clear at the top.

Hyperactive husbands

1

2

3

Drawing the line

Wiring up the fence to deter stray cats

Acceptable ☐

Not Acceptable ☐

Great figures

9 9 2
8 8

Epic encounters

Two incredibly high buildings to jump off

Made in China

1
2
3

Best mates

Tammy

Oliver

Siân

Dilemmas

When contemplating a visit to the Theatre

Chekhov ☐

The Panto ☐

A dog's dinner

It really could happen

All buildings will be made of gingerbread to make them just as strong but much nicer to eat in an emergency.

Holding forth - Slow lorries

The wood for the trees

Marks out of 10

Airship ☐
Burglar Alarm ☐
Celluloid ☐
Encyclopedia ☐
Helicopter ☐
Margarine ☐
Porcelain ☐
Rubber ☐
Soap ☐
Television ☐

Over-reactions

When the well known magician and illusionist turned up the only thing to disappear was ...

Forged signatures

Signed

Name in Block Capitals

The void

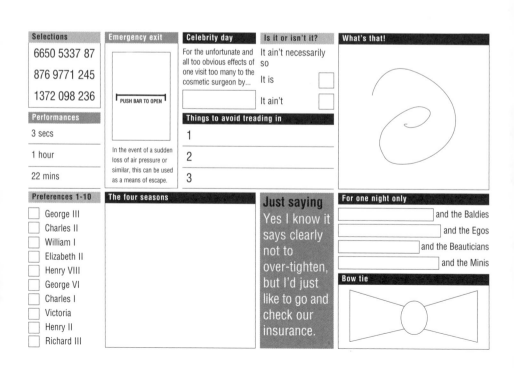

Selections

6650 5337 87

876 9771 245

1372 098 236

Performances

3 secs

1 hour

22 mins

Preferences 1-10

☐ George III
☐ Charles II
☐ William I
☐ Elizabeth II
☐ Henry VIII
☐ George VI
☐ Charles I
☐ Victoria
☐ Henry II
☐ Richard III

Emergency exit

┌ PUSH BAR TO OPEN ┐

In the event of a sudden loss of air pressure or similar, this can be used as a means of escape.

The four seasons

Celebrity day

For the unfortunate and all too obvious effects of one visit too many to the cosmetic surgeon by...

Things to avoid treading in

1

2

3

Is it or isn't it?

It ain't necessarily so

It is ☐

It ain't ☐

Just saying

Yes I know it says clearly not to over-tighten, but I'd just like to go and check our insurance.

What's that!

For one night only

☐ and the Baldies

☐ and the Egos

☐ and the Beauticians

☐ and the Minis

Bow tie

Stupid things to do

....
....
....
....

Feathered friends

1 _____

2 _____

3 _____

Bad timing

The eclipse was only going to happen every few hundred years but the astronomer was...

The void

Official licence

Name

Licence

Purpose

Suburbia

Means the same

Silly

Dissolve

Banal

Preferences 1-10

☐ Muscadet
☐ Chianti
☐ Chardonnay
☐ Merlot
☐ Zinfandel
☐ Sauternes
☐ Fitou
☐ Burgundy
☐ Chablis
☐ Rioja

Choices

Particularly exciting sports to watch on telly

The long lens

That'll be the day!

A contraption with long sticky out things and a driver will enable us to travel around in the air.

Dilemmas

Which science to try to understand

Astrophysics ☐

Aeronautics ☐

Shape it up

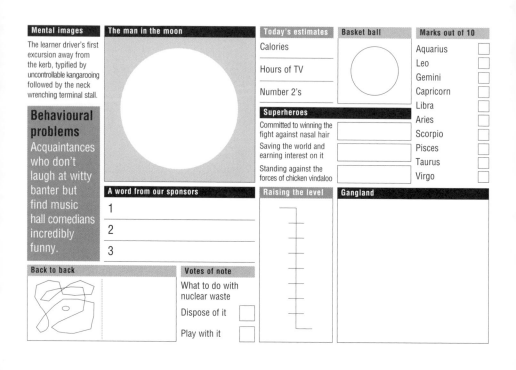

Mental images

The learner driver's first excursion away from the kerb, typified by uncontrollable kangarooing followed by the neck wrenching terminal stall.

Behavioural problems

Acquaintances who don't laugh at witty banter but find music hall comedians incredibly funny.

The man in the moon

A word from our sponsors

1

2

3

Back to back

Today's estimates

Calories

Hours of TV

Number 2's

Superheroes

Committed to winning the fight against nasal hair

Saving the world and earning interest on it

Standing against the forces of chicken vindaloo

Votes of note

What to do with nuclear waste

Dispose of it

Play with it

Basket ball

Raising the level

Gangland

Marks out of 10

Aquarius

Leo

Gemini

Capricorn

Libra

Aries

Scorpio

Pisces

Taurus

Virgo

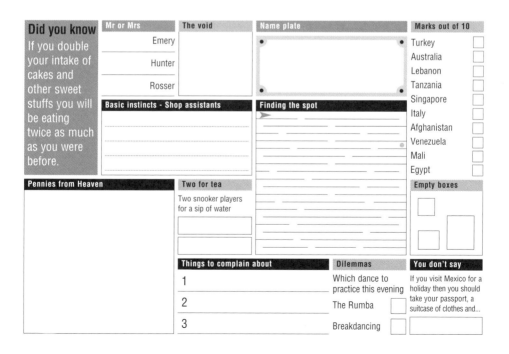

Did you know If you double your intake of cakes and other sweet stuffs you will be eating twice as much as you were before.

Mr or Mrs
Emery
Hunter
Rosser

The void

Name plate

Marks out of 10
Turkey
Australia
Lebanon
Tanzania
Singapore
Italy
Afghanistan
Venezuela
Mali
Egypt

Basic instincts - Shop assistants

Finding the spot

Pennies from Heaven

Two for tea
Two snooker players for a sip of water

Empty boxes

Things to complain about
1
2
3

Dilemmas
Which dance to practice this evening

The Rumba

Breakdancing

You don't say
If you visit Mexico for a holiday then you should take your passport, a suitcase of clothes and...

Steady Eddie

Preferences 1-10

- [ ] Dalmatian
- [ ] Yorkshire Terrier
- [ ] Labrador
- [ ] Poodle
- [ ] Rottweiler
- [ ] Spaniel
- [ ] Dachshund
- [ ] Doberman
- [ ] Shih-tzu
- [ ] Boxer

Sod's Law

I joined the shortest queue but was behind the bloke whose goods had lost their bar codes and who clearly was not familiar with money.

Definitive definitions

	(adj) The feeling of cold gravy on the hand
	(n) A group of people moving aimlessly
	(v) To fall from grace in a spectacular way

From A to B

The shower curtain

Suggestions box

Preferred speed for The London Eye

Gently turning ☐

Very, very fast ☐

Dodgy names for a baby

1 _____

2 _____

3 _____

Fantasy mudwrestling

	V	
	V	
	V	
	V	

Surfing

Yesterday

Today

Tomorrow

Time to go home

A fight at the opera

There was a right royal rumpus at the opera tonight when a voice from the Royal Box yelled...

Dilemmas

What to do if you see an accident

Report it ☐

Run off ☐

The void

Sharp fruits

1 _____

2 _____

3 _____

Spatial awareness

The first half

Tommy
_____

Chimney
_____

Farm
_____

Below the belt

Preferences 1-10

☐ Cotton
☐ Paper
☐ Leather
☐ Fruit
☐ Wood
☐ Sugar
☐ Wool
☐ Bronze
☐ Pottery
☐ Tin

Occurrences

Scones, cream and jam were considered very decadent, cattle wore coats and it was essential to sing around the piano.

An embarrassing moment

Doublers

Things that are known to smell very similar

☐

☐

The big deal

The Prime Minister is going to drop round to ask for your considered opinion on the latest...

Comfort gauge

Very Uncomfy   Very Comfy

Charting progress - Mistakes

Cock Ups

Mon   Tues   Wed   Thurs   Fri

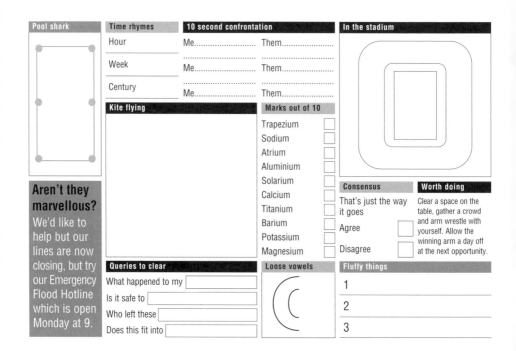

Pool shark

Time rhymes

Hour

Week

Century

10 second confrontation

Me....................... Them.....................

Me....................... Them.....................

Me....................... Them.....................

In the stadium

Kite flying

Marks out of 10

Trapezium ☐
Sodium ☐
Atrium ☐
Aluminium ☐
Solarium ☐
Calcium ☐
Titanium ☐
Barium ☐
Potassium ☐
Magnesium ☐

Consensus

That's just the way it goes

Agree ☐

Disagree

Worth doing

Clear a space on the table, gather a crowd and arm wrestle with yourself. Allow the winning arm a day off at the next opportunity. ☐

Aren't they marvellous?

We'd like to help but our lines are now closing, but try our Emergency Flood Hotline which is open Monday at 9.

Queries to clear

What happened to my ☐

Is it safe to ☐

Who left these ☐

Does this fit into ☐

Loose vowels

Fluffy things

1

2

3

In order to make the day pass more pleasantly it has been decreed that the Noise of the Day is...

Floral tribute

Marks out of 10

Amoco Cadiz ☐
Atlantic Empress ☐
Braer ☐
Exxon Valdez ☐
Khorg 5 ☐
Othello ☐
Sea Empress ☐
Sea Star ☐
Torrey Canyon ☐
World Glory ☐

Through the porthole

Word association

Joyful

Settler

Masseur

Multi-tasking

Replace some of the old plumbing in the bathroom and manage to avoid a huge leaking disaster in the kitchen.

Barmy army

Desires - Sexual activities

Statuesque

Poor performers

Leading by miles then dropped the baton

Good eggs

1

2

3

Dilemmas

The best way to put the rubbish out

In sacks ☐

Insult it ☐

The void

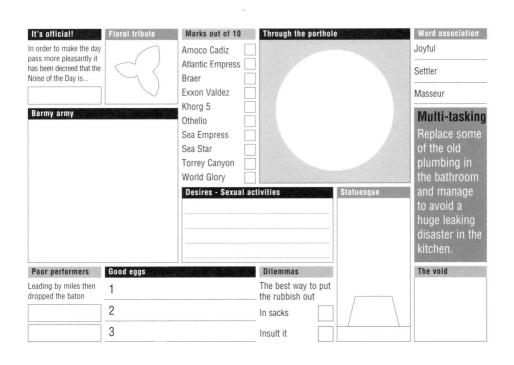

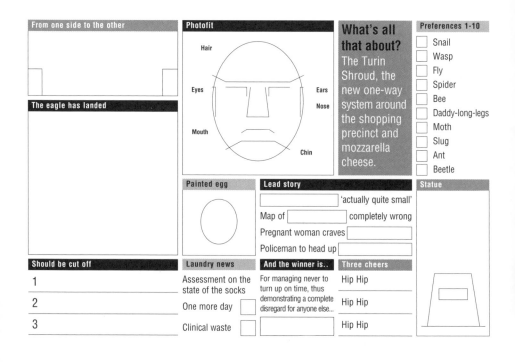

From one side to the other

The eagle has landed

Should be cut off

1

2

3

Photofit

Hair

Eyes

Mouth

Ears

Nose

Chin

Painted egg

Laundry news

Assessment on the state of the socks

One more day

Clinical waste

What's all that about?
The Turin Shroud, the new one-way system around the shopping precinct and mozzarella cheese.

Lead story

'actually quite small'

Map of _____ completely wrong

Pregnant woman craves _____

Policeman to head up _____

And the winner is..

For managing never to turn up on time, thus demonstrating a complete disregard for anyone else...

Preferences 1-10

☐ Snail
☐ Wasp
☐ Fly
☐ Spider
☐ Bee
☐ Daddy-long-legs
☐ Moth
☐ Slug
☐ Ant
☐ Beetle

Statue

Three cheers

Hip Hip

Hip Hip

Hip Hip

Star turns	Dilemmas	Spectacle wearers	X ray	Poles apart

Star turns

Julian

Diane

Anthony

Dilemmas

New colour for the Eiffel Tower

Fluorescent Pink ☐

British Racing Green ☐

Spectacle wearers

1 _____

2 _____

3 _____

X ray

X

Poles apart

Friends who could never live in the same house

☐

The void

Great events in history

- - - - - - - - - - - - - - - -
- - - - - - - - - - - - - - - -
- - - - - - - - - - - - - - - -
- - - - - - - - - - - - - - - -

Thought for the day

A bird in the hand is not worth two in the bush but surely only what someone is willing to pay for it.

The sack race

Preferences 1-10

☐ Jailhouse Rock
☐ The Young Ones
☐ Get Back
☐ Two Tribes
☐ The Fly
☐ Some Might Say
☐ Two Become One
☐ Stand and Deliver
☐ Never Forget
☐ Fairground

Join the dots

Price fixing - I bought the football club

Date _____

Pay _____

The Sum of _____ £ _____

_____

1345 673 2759 02

Bad behaviour

There was a disturbance in the dentist's waiting room earlier today when a patient exclaimed...

☐

Born to run

To be considered

Keeping an Emerald Tree Boa as a pet

No way, José ☐

Slip me some skin ☐

Recycling

Collect several used sheets, tear them up into small pieces and use as ticker-tape to welcome a friend back from the shops.

Sandwich board

The Big OFFER

Spotty face

Favourite friends' mothers

1 _____

2 _____

3 _____

It's only B words

B _____

B _____

B _____

Basic needs

☐ to restore order

☐ to balance things out

☐ to frighten the neighbours

☐ to clear the sinuses

Planned exercise

Wheezing

Mon Tues Wed Thurs Fri Sat Sun

Just saying

You really shouldn't have set sail if you were having to bail out before you left the harbour, but then again, what do I know.

Border crossing

Marks out of 10

Arabic ☐

French ☐

Swahili ☐

Russian ☐

Mandarin ☐

Greek ☐

Portuguese ☐

Hindustani ☐

German ☐

Italian ☐

Portrait gallery - Lionel Richie

Opposites

Full
_____

Alive
_____

Lost
_____

Marks out of 10

Buckingham ☐
Derbyshire ☐
Durham ☐
Hertfordshire ☐
Kent ☐
Northampton ☐
Somerset ☐
Surrey ☐
North Yorkshire ☐
Worcestershire ☐

Options

Authors to quote if you want to impress

[   ]

[   ]

Certifiable

Awarded to

for their

_____

_____

Signed

_____

The truth hurts - Oscar winners

....
....
....
....

Parasites

1 _____

2 _____

3 _____

Dilemmas

What should be on our identity cards?

Name and picture ☐

The 5 of Clubs ☐

Finish it off

Perfect timing

The stable door got slammed well and truly shut just before the horse started to become a little agitated.

Shoulder to shoulder

Rubber stamp

There was agreement at the cricket club that when fielding at silly mid off, you have to wear ...

[   ]

The void

- [ ] Drilling
- [ ] Selling
- [ ] Milling
- [ ] Telling
- [ ] Willing
- [ ] Yelling
- [ ] Spilling
- [ ] Felling
- [ ] Billing
- [ ] Spelling

Choose one

55 623

995 17

What's what

Made of bread and capable of supporting a small family

Large, pink and worthy of a mention on TV

Designed to create total disruption in the bathroom

A dubious ending

erly

ed

ate

Up and under

Today's word

For today, or until a decision is made otherwise, the day's nominated word is...

Behavioural problems
The considered philosophy of people who wear heavy coats, gloves and warm hats at the height of summer.

Good darts

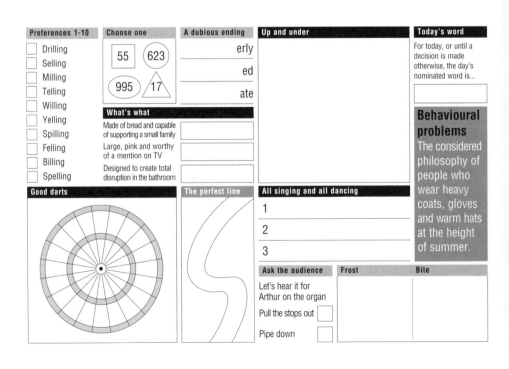

The perfect line

All singing and all dancing

1

2

3

Ask the audience

Let's hear it for Arthur on the organ

Pull the stops out [ ]

Pipe down [ ]

Frost

Bite

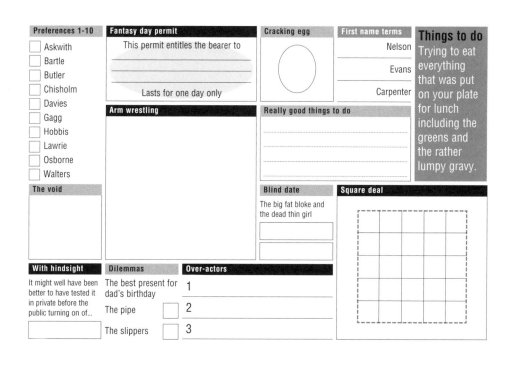

Preferences 1-10

- [ ] Askwith
- [ ] Bartle
- [ ] Butler
- [ ] Chisholm
- [ ] Davies
- [ ] Gagg
- [ ] Hobbis
- [ ] Lawrie
- [ ] Osborne
- [ ] Walters

The void

Fantasy day permit

This permit entitles the bearer to

Lasts for one day only

Arm wrestling

Cracking egg

Really good things to do

Blind date

The big fat bloke and
the dead thin girl

First name terms

Nelson

Evans

Carpenter

Things to do

Trying to eat
everything
that was put
on your plate
for lunch
including the
greens and
the rather
lumpy gravy.

Square deal

With hindsight

It might well have been
better to have tested it
in private before the
public turning on of...

Dilemmas

The best present for
dad's birthday

The pipe

The slippers

Over-actors

1

2

3

Definitive definitions

	(*n*) A particularly thorough nose pick
	(*v*) Walking on the cracks in the pavement
	(*v*) To rush for, but just miss, the train

Rewind

Sod's Law

Two days before our skiing holiday and Jamie's managed to break his ankle by falling over his dog.

Possessions

- Pliers ☐
- Clip board ☐
- Linen basket ☐
- Squash racket ☐
- Paint ☐
- Whistle ☐
- Herb rack ☐
- Cigarette lighter ☐
- Spare keys ☐
- Toilet brush ☐

Trapped wind

Mythical beings

1 _____

2 _____

3 _____

The verdict

Stealing glasses from the pub

Guilty ☐

Not Guilty ☐

Watch it

You what!?

So you're going to go to the doctor and he's going to stick a tube up your arse and fill it full of warm water. And this is going to make you feel better?

Corporate logo

Open to offers

Yesterday

Today

Tomorrow

Impressive scores

In the wind tunnel

High profile prisoners

1

2

3

The void

Dilemmas

Your dinner guest for the evening

Dr Jekyll ☐

Mr Hyde ☐

Half and half

Thinking ahead

When about to give an important presentation, it is always a really good idea to check...

Marks out of 10

Don Ameche ☐
Glenn Close ☐
Brad Pitt ☐
Robert De Niro ☐
Diana Dors ☐
Richard Gere ☐
Will Hay ☐
Rick Moranis ☐
Mickey Rooney ☐
Sylvester Stallone ☐

Launchtime

The second half

Camera

Day

Sandwich

What a total waste of time

Arguing that a film actor is some kind of 'social worker' that can help mere mortals understand their own life.

Reality check

Time	Place
Who's in front	
Who's behind	
Who's talking	

Pairing up

They are very different but it seems to work

Celebrations - Buying the first house

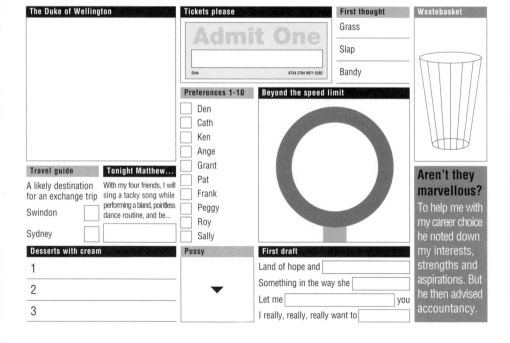

The Duke of Wellington

Tickets please

Admit One

Date   8734 2764 9071 5282

First thought

Grass

Slap

Bandy

Wastebasket

Travel guide

A likely destination
for an exchange trip

Swindon

Sydney

Tonight Matthew...

With my four friends, I will
sing a tacky song while
performing a bland, pointless
dance routine, and be...

Preferences 1-10

Den
Cath
Ken
Ange
Grant
Pat
Frank
Peggy
Roy
Sally

Beyond the speed limit

**Aren't they
marvellous?**

To help me with
my career choice
he noted down
my interests,
strengths and
aspirations. But
he then advised
accountancy.

Desserts with cream

1

2

3

Pussy

▼

First draft

Land of hope and

Something in the way she

Let me   you

I really, really, really want to

Vice

Marvellous

Dog

Today's the day

For pointing from afar at everyone that travels on the bus, train, tram or other forms of public transport.

The void

Portrait of a lion

Headlines

The Daily
NEWS

Preferences 1-10

☐ Utah
☐ Wisconsin
☐ California
☐ Hawaii
☐ Alabama
☐ Delaware
☐ Kansas
☐ Ohio
☐ New York
☐ Wyoming

Offering advice

....
....
....
....

Dilemmas

How to handle the irritating housemate

Kid gloves ☐

Boxing gloves ☐

Notable battles

1

2

3

Timeless

12
9 ● 3
6

Broken promises

Announcement

We apologise that the buffet has had to be cancelled, but all the pies have been eaten by...

Heavy hitters

The final of the all time heavyweight competition

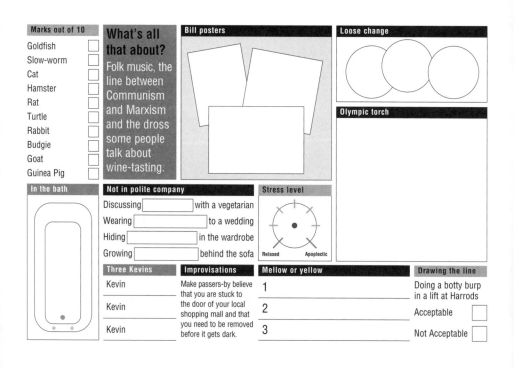

Marks out of 10

Goldfish
Slow-worm
Cat
Hamster
Rat
Turtle
Rabbit
Budgie
Goat
Guinea Pig

What's all that about?
Folk music, the line between Communism and Marxism and the dross some people talk about wine-tasting.

Bill posters

Loose change

Olympic torch

In the bath

Not in polite company

Discussing [   ] with a vegetarian
Wearing [   ] to a wedding
Hiding [   ] in the wardrobe
Growing [   ] behind the sofa

Stress level

Relaxed   Apoplectic

Three Kevins

Kevin

Kevin

Kevin

Improvisations

Make passers-by believe that you are stuck to the door of your local shopping mall and that you need to be removed before it gets dark.

Mellow or yellow

1
2
3

Drawing the line

Doing a botty burp in a lift at Harrods

Acceptable [   ]

Not Acceptable [   ]

Great figures	Epic encounters	Great virtues		Best mates	Dilemmas
10 0 0	The small man against the huge conglomerate	1		Rhys	The best place to find yourself stuck
		2		Elizabeth	A rock ☐
		3		Alan	A hard place ☐

Day release

It really could happen
Lucifer, the Prince of Darkness, will visit the earth to offer advice on how things could be improved.

Holding forth - Phone messages

....
....
....
....

Over the hill

Marks out of 10

Oil ☐
Olives ☐
Opera ☐
Orange ☐
Opinion Polls ☐
Opulence ☐
Oman ☐
Owls ☐
Oxygen ☐
Oysters ☐

Over-reactions

On starting the 17th series of Big Brother, the producers were confident that it would...

Ransom demand

_____ ☐
_____
_____
_____

The void

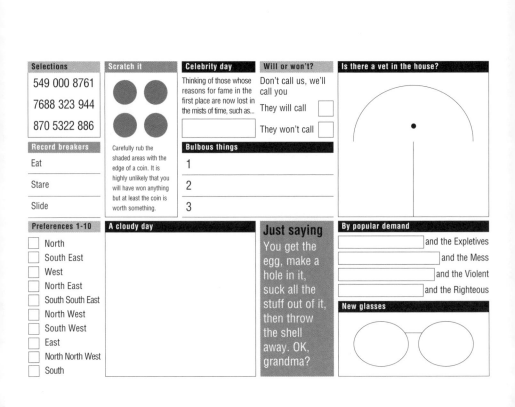

Selections

549 000 8761

7688 323 944

870 5322 886

Record breakers

Eat

Stare

Slide

Preferences 1-10

- [ ] North
- [ ] South East
- [ ] West
- [ ] North East
- [ ] South South East
- [ ] North West
- [ ] South West
- [ ] East
- [ ] North North West
- [ ] South

Scratch it

Carefully rub the shaded areas with the edge of a coin. It is highly unlikely that you will have won anything but at least the coin is worth something.

Celebrity day

Thinking of those whose reasons for fame in the first place are now lost in the mists of time, such as...

Bulbous things

1

2

3

A cloudy day

Will or won't?

Don't call us, we'll call you

They will call

They won't call

Just saying

You get the egg, make a hole in it, suck all the stuff out of it, then throw the shell away. OK, grandma?

Is there a vet in the house?

By popular demand

and the Expletives

and the Mess

and the Violent

and the Righteous

New glasses

Stupid things to do

Marlon Brando films

1

2

3

Bad timing

It would have been a very pleasant safari if they hadn't been in the wrong place and attacked by...

The void

Living on the edge

Daily pass

| Name |
| Sex |
| Mood |
| Visiting |

Means the same

Lucifer

Mandatory

Brew

Preferences 1-10

☐ Alligator
☐ Chameleon
☐ Gecko
☐ Iguana
☐ Skink
☐ Tortoise
☐ Sea Turtle
☐ Viper
☐ Python
☐ Lizard

Choices

Drinks to give you a bad head in the morning

Tonight's telly

◀ ● ▶

That'll be the day!

We will all go to a large dark room with seats to watch huge moving images for entertainment purposes.

Dilemmas

The best way to deter unexpected visitors

Curtains closed ☐

A moat ☐

Shape it up

The man who, in striding through the door, catches the lining of his jacket on the handle and lurches to a halt, with egg on his face and a sleeve in his hand.

Behavioural problems

Those who enthusiastically embrace the same advice from paid therapists when they've rejected yours.

One for the CD collection

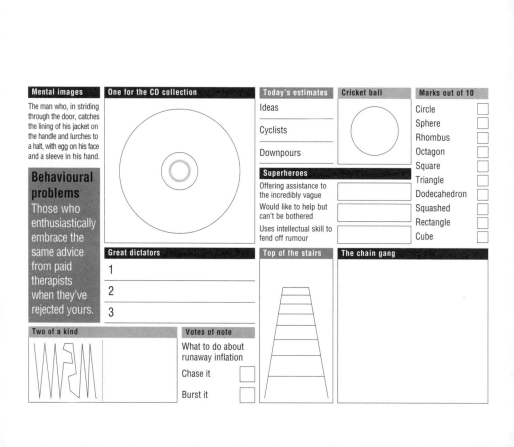

Great dictators

1

2

3

Two of a kind

Today's estimates

Ideas

Cyclists

Downpours

Superheroes

Offering assistance to the incredibly vague

Would like to help but can't be bothered

Uses intellectual skill to fend off rumour

Top of the stairs

Votes of note

What to do about runaway inflation

Chase it ☐

Burst it ☐

Cricket ball

Marks out of 10

Circle ☐
Sphere ☐
Rhombus ☐
Octagon ☐
Square ☐
Triangle ☐
Dodecahedron ☐
Squashed ☐
Rectangle ☐
Cube ☐

The chain gang

Did you know

When it gets dark in the evening it is much more difficult to see than when it is lighter, which is usually earlier in the day.

Mr or Mrs

Kemp

Cocker

Powell

Basic instincts - Smelly people

The void

Behind closed doors

Director of androgynous, limp wristed flouncing about everywhere

Choose the way in

Entrance 1

Entrance 2

Marks out of 10

Uranium ☐
Sodium ☐
Palladium ☐
Aluminium ☐
Helium ☐
Calcium ☐
Radium ☐
Plutonium ☐
Magnesium ☐
Potassium ☐

Flower power

Two for tea

Actors to share a cheese flan and salad

Empty boxes

Fast cars

1

2

3

Dilemmas

Today's important decision is between

Art

Literature

You don't say

When setting off to walk to the North Pole remember to pack a thermos, anorak and...

The wrinkly wrinkle

Preferences 1-10

- [ ] 100m
- [ ] Long Jump
- [ ] Shot Put
- [ ] High Jump
- [ ] 400m
- [ ] 110m Hurdles
- [ ] Discus
- [ ] Pole Vault
- [ ] Javelin
- [ ] 1500m

Sod's Law

After drinking warm, flat beer for two hours, somebody spilt guacamole down my front and now I'm in the kitchen with a depressive.

Definitive definitions

	(*adj*) A wildly inaccurate weather forecast
	(*n*) Food consumed well after its eat by date
	(*v*) To open a can of overly effervescent beer

Constellations

Make the bed

Suggestions box

To brighten up the living room

Flowers [ ]

A bonfire [ ]

New Year resolutions

1 _____

2 _____

3 _____

Sons and lovers

	+	
	+	
	+	
	+	

Radio choice

Yesterday

Today

Tomorrow

Spare time

Animal crackers

There was complete bedlam at a pet shop today when the owner's alligator started chewing...

Preferred method of getting to work

Tube ☐

Unicycle ☐

The void

To be done again and again

1 _____

2 _____

3 _____

The bathroom

The door

The bath

The window

The first half

Bowling

Traffic

Banana

Every dog has his day

Preferences 1-10

☐ Raymond Blanc
☐ Isabella Beeton
☐ Keith Floyd
☐ Loyd Grossman
☐ Nigella Lawson
☐ Gary Rhodes
☐ Delia Smith
☐ Rick Stein
☐ Anton Mosimann
☐ Gordon Ramsay

Occurrences

Neanderthals mysteriously disappeared from the face of the earth, but after a damp start it turned out nice again.

The big deal

Wouldn't it be good if Wayne Rooney came round and asked for you to help with his...

Relief gauge

Slight   Blowing a Stack

An embarrassing moment

Doublers

Ways of stirring a very large vat of soup

The long way out

In ——————

———— Out

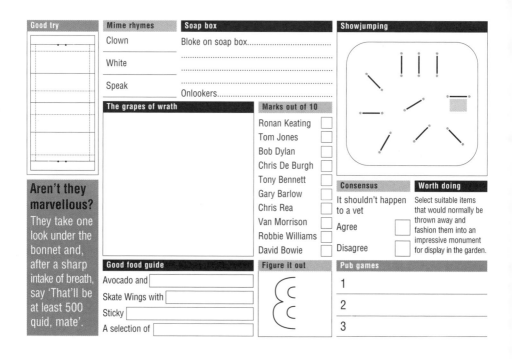

Good try

Mime rhymes

Clown

White

Speak

Aren't they marvellous?

They take one look under the bonnet and, after a sharp intake of breath, say 'That'll be at least 500 quid, mate'.

The grapes of wrath

Good food guide

Avocado and

Skate Wings with

Sticky

A selection of

Soap box

Bloke on soap box.......................................

....

....

....

Onlookers..

Marks out of 10

Ronan Keating

Tom Jones

Bob Dylan

Chris De Burgh

Tony Bennett

Gary Barlow

Chris Rea

Van Morrison

Robbie Williams

David Bowie

Figure it out

Showjumping

Consensus

It shouldn't happen to a vet

Agree

Disagree

Worth doing

Select suitable items that would normally be thrown away and fashion them into an impressive monument for display in the garden.

Pub games

1

2

3

It's official!

In order to make the day pass more pleasantly it has been decreed that the Cheese of the Day is...

Leaves

Marks out of 10

- John Bunyan
- Charles Dickens
- Roddy Doyle
- Henry Fielding
- Robert Graves
- Erica Jong
- Jack London
- Mary Shelley
- Mark Twain
- Virginia Woolf

Splish

Word association

Fungus

Tartan

Grill

Multi-tasking

Attempt to pay Peter that to which he is legally entitled without having to resort to robbing Paul to effect the transaction.

A frosty reception

Desires - The perfect retreat

Sports day

Poor performers

Politicians who promised but failed spectacularly

Types of pastry

1

2

3

Dilemmas

To remove nasty, unsightly stains

Big scrubber

Flamethrower

Shooting

The void

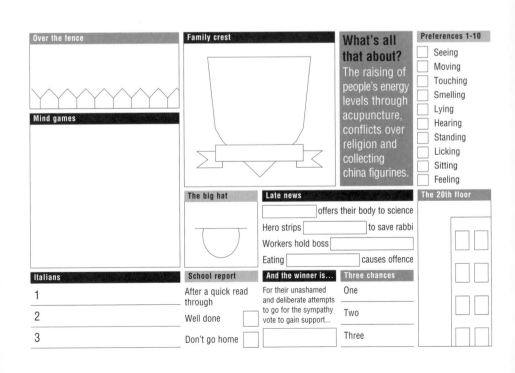

Over the fence

Mind games

Italians

1

2

3

Family crest

The big hat

School report

After a quick read through

Well done

Don't go home

What's all that about?
The raising of people's energy levels through acupuncture, conflicts over religion and collecting china figurines.

Late news

offers their body to science

Hero strips [   ] to save rabbi

Workers hold boss [   ]

Eating [   ] causes offence

And the winner is...
For their unashamed and deliberate attempts to go for the sympathy vote to gain support...

Preferences 1-10

☐ Seeing
☐ Moving
☐ Touching
☐ Smelling
☐ Lying
☐ Hearing
☐ Standing
☐ Licking
☐ Sitting
☐ Feeling

The 20th floor

Three chances

One

Two

Three

Eve

Quincy

Rachel

To wear when the rain is pouring down

Plastic Mac ☐

Fish Suit ☐

1

2

3

E

Previously unavailable flavours of crisp

Thought for the day

Who says you can't have your cake and eat it, what else are you meant to do with a nice slice of cake?

☐ Acupuncture
☐ Aromatherapy
☐ Homeopathy
☐ Hypnotherapy
☐ Meditation
☐ Naturopathy
☐ Osteopathy
☐ Reflexology
☐ Shiatsu
☐ Yoga

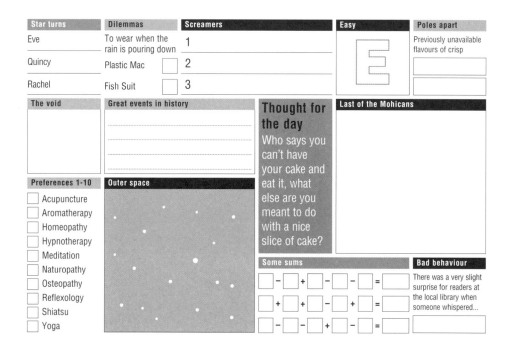

☐ − ☐ + ☐ − ☐ − ☐ = ☐

☐ + ☐ + ☐ − ☐ + ☐ = ☐

☐ − ☐ − ☐ + ☐ − ☐ = ☐

There was a very slight surprise for readers at the local library when someone whispered...

Computer virus

To be considered

If you can't beat them

Join them ☐

Poach them ☐

Recycling

This sheet can be placed under the windscreen wiper of an annoyingly parked car, giving the owner the impression that they've been booked.

This week's offer

BARGAIN BASEMENT

Ugly face

Naughty clothing

1 _____

2 _____

3 _____

It's only Y words

Y _____

Y _____

Y _____

That's the way to do it

	to make it jump
	can cause bleeding
	may reduce weight
	should help flatulence

Predicted interest levels

Alertness

10.00 11.00 12.00 13.00 14.00 15.00 16.00

Just saying

We've come down here and got a result, the lads gave 110% and you can't ask for anything more at the end of the day.

The airline

Marks out of 10

Manchester Utd ☐
Barcelona ☐
Ajax ☐
Benfica ☐
Juventus ☐
Arsenal ☐
Real Madrid ☐
Bayern Munich ☐
AC Milan ☐
Rapid Vienna ☐

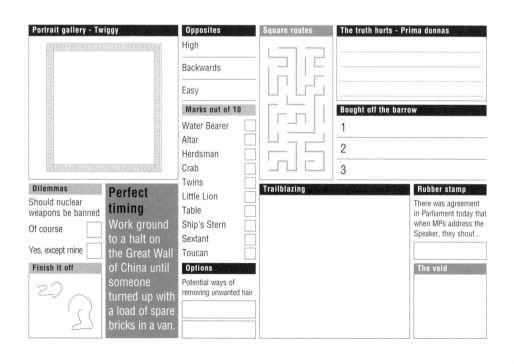

Portrait gallery - Twiggy

Opposites

High

Backwards

Easy

Square routes

The truth hurts - Prima donnas

Bought off the barrow

1

2

3

Marks out of 10

Water Bearer

Altar

Herdsman

Crab

Twins

Little Lion

Table

Ship's Stern

Sextant

Toucan

Dilemmas

Should nuclear weapons be banned

Of course

Yes, except mine

Finish it off

Perfect timing

Work ground to a halt on the Great Wall of China until someone turned up with a load of spare bricks in a van.

Options

Potential ways of removing unwanted hair

Trailblazing

Rubber stamp

There was agreement in Parliament today that when MPs address the Speaker, they shout...

The void

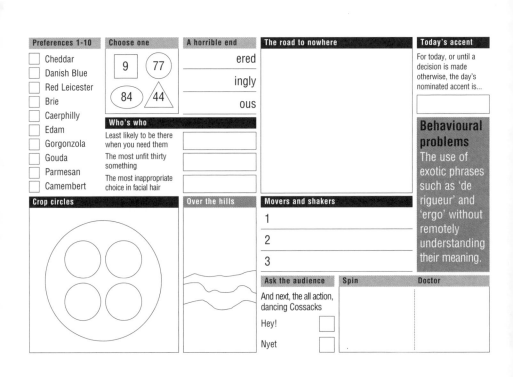

Preferences 1-10

- ☐ Cheddar
- ☐ Danish Blue
- ☐ Red Leicester
- ☐ Brie
- ☐ Caerphilly
- ☐ Edam
- ☐ Gorgonzola
- ☐ Gouda
- ☐ Parmesan
- ☐ Camembert

Choose one

9　77

84　44

A horrible end

_____ ered

_____ ingly

_____ ous

Who's who

Least likely to be there when you need them

The most unfit thirty something

The most inappropriate choice in facial hair

The road to nowhere

Today's accent

For today, or until a decision is made otherwise, the day's nominated accent is...

Behavioural problems

The use of exotic phrases such as 'de rigueur' and 'ergo' without remotely understanding their meaning.

Crop circles

Over the hills

Movers and shakers

1 _____

2 _____

3 _____

Ask the audience

And next, the all action, dancing Cossacks

Hey!

Nyet

Spin

Doctor

Preferences 1-10

- [ ] Periwinkle
- [ ] Cockle
- [ ] Oyster
- [ ] Scallop
- [ ] Squid
- [ ] Krill
- [ ] Lobster
- [ ] Shrimp
- [ ] Prawn
- [ ] Mussel

Tickets please

Admit One

Gold Club Member   8734 2764 9071 5282

Jacket and tie

The void

Flat as a pancake

First name terms

Herbert

Chaplin

Owen

Really good things to do

Things to do

Wherever you are wait for somebody to make a small mistake, not anything serious, then criticise them unrelentingly.

Blind date

From the celebrity C list, the beauty and the beast

Pixelated image

With hindsight

If you were going to invite a guest to talk on public morality, why the hell did you ask...

Dilemmas

Choosing a name for the new baby

Apple

Banana

Simple sciences

1

2

3

Definitive definitions

(*v*) To feign an expression of surprise

(*n*) Huge amounts of financial information

(*n*) The place where lost car keys are always found

Press the pause button

Sod's Law

I found a great position on the grassy knoll, saw the President's car coming and then somebody went and blew his head off.

Possessions

Dried flowers ☐
Slug killer ☐
Toilet brush ☐
Alarm clock ☐
Clothes pegs ☐
Table tennis bat ☐
The Bible ☐
Filing cabinet ☐
Camera ☐
Extension lead ☐

Bat out of Hell

Dull people

1 _____

2 _____

3 _____

The verdict

Lying to avoid being in big trouble

Guilty ☐

Not guilty ☐

Status report

Day

Date

Time

Venue

Conditions

Coat

Hat

Signed

You what!?

So you've got a country of your own but you think you'd like another one, and so you're just going to march in with a huge army and take it.

Media logo

Sandwiches

Yesterday

Today

Tomorrow

Rear view mirror

The Paparazzi strike again

Books in the Bible

1 _____

2 _____

3 _____

The void

Dilemmas

To request a little music later on

Mr Lennon ☐

Mr McCartney ☐

Marks out of 10

Bush Snr ☐
Nixon ☐
Kennedy ☐
Carter ☐
Truman ☐
Clinton ☐
Bush Jnr ☐
Eisenhower ☐
Reagan ☐
Roosevelt ☐

Rich pickings

The second half

Traffic

Course

Way

Half and half

Thinking ahead

When walking back from a night out, be alert, on your guard and always carry ...

What a total waste of time

It really isn't worth starting to look for a needle in a haystack because you can easily get another one.

Essential activities

This Morning

This Afternoon

This Evening

Pairing up

A hairy black thing and a slippery green thing

Celebrations - Retirement

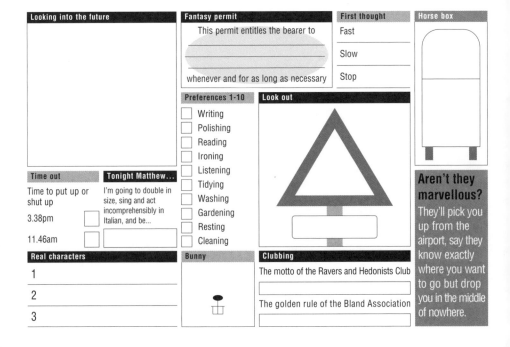

Looking into the future

Fantasy permit

This permit entitles the bearer to

whenever and for as long as necessary

First thought

Fast

Slow

Stop

Horse box

Time out

Time to put up or shut up

3.38pm

11.46am

Tonight Matthew...

I'm going to double in size, sing and act incomprehensibly in Italian, and be...

Preferences 1-10

Writing
Polishing
Reading
Ironing
Listening
Tidying
Washing
Gardening
Resting
Cleaning

Look out

Aren't they marvellous?

They'll pick you up from the airport, say they know exactly where you want to go but drop you in the middle of nowhere.

Real characters

1

2

3

Bunny

Clubbing

The motto of the Ravers and Hedonists Club

The golden rule of the Bland Association

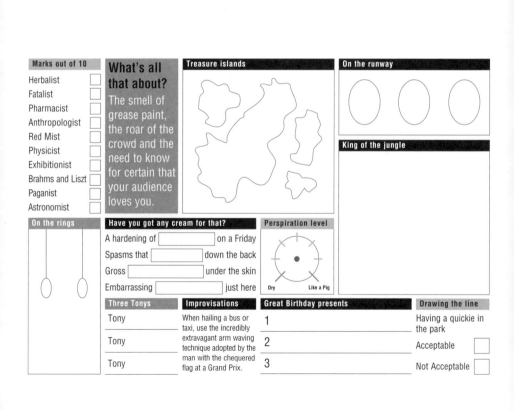

Marks out of 10

- Herbalist ☐
- Fatalist ☐
- Pharmacist ☐
- Anthropologist ☐
- Red Mist ☐
- Physicist ☐
- Exhibitionist ☐
- Brahms and Liszt ☐
- Paganist ☐
- Astronomist ☐

What's all that about?

The smell of grease paint, the roar of the crowd and the need to know for certain that your audience loves you.

Treasure islands

On the runway

King of the jungle

On the rings

Have you got any cream for that?

A hardening of [ ] on a Friday

Spasms that [ ] down the back

Gross [ ] under the skin

Embarrassing [ ] just here

Perspiration level

Dry   Like a Pig

Three Tonys

Tony

Tony

Tony

Improvisations

When hailing a bus or taxi, use the incredibly extravagant arm waving technique adopted by the man with the chequered flag at a Grand Prix.

Great Birthday presents

1

2

3

Drawing the line

Having a quickie in the park

Acceptable ☐

Not Acceptable ☐

Great figures	Epic encounters	Baseball teams		Best mates	Dilemmas

Great figures

247
84

Epic encounters

Two giants of the sporting world do battle

Baseball teams

1

2

3

Best mates

Sophia

Maurice

Fiona

Dilemmas

Food to eat at the Dog and Duck

The Dog ☐

The Duck ☐

Total nothingness

It really could happen

Plans are underway to develop an underground city for people that are afraid of the sky and don't like birds.

Holding forth - Speed cameras

The tide coming in

Marks out of 10

Wombat ☐
Bison ☐
Chimpanzee ☐
Gopher ☐
Marmoset ☐
Racoon ☐
Shrew ☐
Weasel ☐
Sperm Whale ☐
Echidna ☐

The Void

Over-reactions

Immediately following the election results, the new Prime Minister said that they would be...

Important labelling

Dangerous Animals

Selections

K **L** *M* **N**
O **P** *Q* **R**
S **T** *U* **V**
W **X** *Y* **Z**

Personal bests

3 Darts

Snooker Break

M25

Preferences 1-10

☐ Avocado
☐ Nectarine
☐ Pear
☐ Melon
☐ Peach
☐ Strawberry
☐ Banana
☐ Apple
☐ Cumquat
☐ Raspberry

Quiet speaker

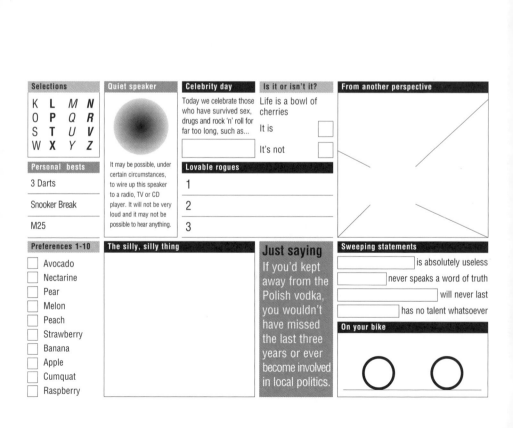

It may be possible, under certain circumstances, to wire up this speaker to a radio, TV or CD player. It will not be very loud and it may not be possible to hear anything.

The silly, silly thing

Celebrity day

Today we celebrate those who have survived sex, drugs and rock 'n' roll for far too long, such as...

Lovable rogues

1

2

3

Is it or isn't it?

Life is a bowl of cherries

It is ☐

It's not ☐

Just saying

If you'd kept away from the Polish vodka, you wouldn't have missed the last three years or ever become involved in local politics.

From another perspective

Sweeping statements

is absolutely useless

never speaks a word of truth

will never last

has no talent whatsoever

On your bike

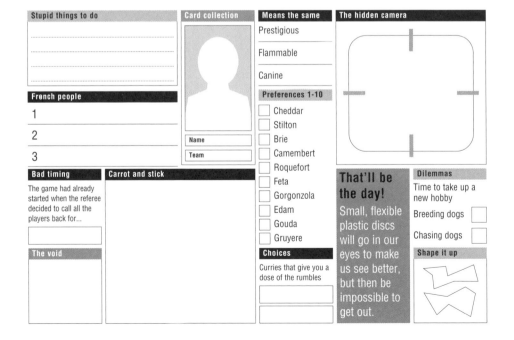

Stupid things to do

....
....
....
....

French people

1

2

3

Bad timing

The game had already started when the referee decided to call all the players back for...

The void

Card collection

Name

Team

Carrot and stick

Means the same

Prestigious

Flammable

Canine

Preferences 1-10

☐ Cheddar
☐ Stilton
☐ Brie
☐ Camembert
☐ Roquefort
☐ Feta
☐ Gorgonzola
☐ Edam
☐ Gouda
☐ Gruyere

Choices

Curries that give you a dose of the rumbles

The hidden camera

That'll be the day!

Small, flexible plastic discs will go in our eyes to make us see better, but then be impossible to get out.

Dilemmas

Time to take up a new hobby

Breeding dogs ☐

Chasing dogs ☐

Shape it up

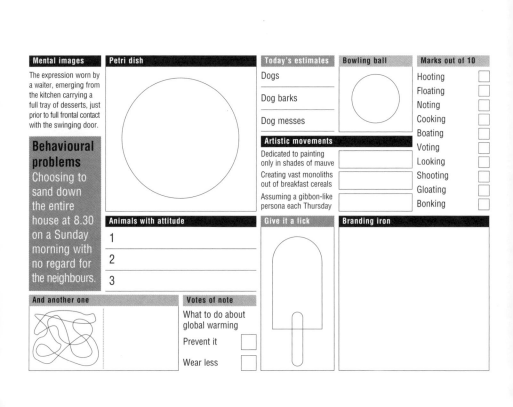

Mental images

The expression worn by a waiter, emerging from the kitchen carrying a full tray of desserts, just prior to full frontal contact with the swinging door.

Behavioural problems

Choosing to sand down the entire house at 8.30 on a Sunday morning with no regard for the neighbours.

Petri dish

And another one

Today's estimates

Dogs

Dog barks

Dog messes

Artistic movements

Dedicated to painting only in shades of mauve

Creating vast monoliths out of breakfast cereals

Assuming a gibbon-like persona each Thursday

Animals with attitude

1

2

3

Votes of note

What to do about global warming

Prevent it

Wear less

Bowling ball

Give it a lick

Marks out of 10

Hooting

Floating

Noting

Cooking

Boating

Voting

Looking

Shooting

Gloating

Bonking

Branding iron

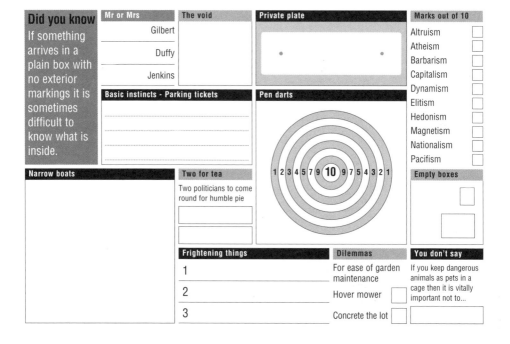

Did you know
If something arrives in a plain box with no exterior markings it is sometimes difficult to know what is inside.

Mr or Mrs
Gilbert
Duffy
Jenkins

Basic instincts - Parking tickets

Narrow boats

The void

Two for tea
Two politicians to come round for humble pie

Frightening things
1
2
3

Private plate

Pen darts

1 2 3 4 5 7 9 **10** 9 7 5 4 3 2 1

Dilemmas
For ease of garden maintenance
Hover mower
Concrete the lot

Marks out of 10
Altruism
Atheism
Barbarism
Capitalism
Dynamism
Elitism
Hedonism
Magnetism
Nationalism
Pacifism

Empty boxes

You don't say
If you keep dangerous animals as pets in a cage then it is vitally important not to...

The elephant explodes

Preferences 1-10

- [ ] Thor
- [ ] Hercules
- [ ] Icarus
- [ ] Merlin
- [ ] Pan
- [ ] Aphrodite
- [ ] Yu the Great
- [ ] Cupid
- [ ] Zeus
- [ ] Neptune

Sod's Law

It hasn't stopped crying for over two hours, I've run out of nappies and now it's been sick all over my fettuccine.

Definitive definitions

	(*adj*) Jeans that have shrunk excessively
	(*n*) Food left on face after messy eating
	(*v*) Riding a bicycle backwards

A bad hand

Grandfather clock

Suggestions box

Method for cooling very hot soup	
Blow on it	☐
Wind tunnel	☐

Causes to die for

1 _____

2 _____

3 _____

Jousting jesters

	V	
	V	
	V	
	V	

Under pressure

Yesterday

Today

Tomorrow

High time

12
9
3
6

Papal problems

There was a crisis of confidence at The Vatican when, on coming out onto the balcony, the Pope...

Dilemmas

Sandwich filling for
brunch at the Zoo

Guacamole ☐

Guano ☐

The void

Under-achievers

1 _____

2 _____

3 _____

Assault on the beach

Enemy ■ ■ ■
Positions

■

The Beach

The Sea

The first half

Driving
_____

Bright
_____

Flag
_____

Whales of fortune

Preferences 1-10

☐ Bacteria
☐ Ballet
☐ Basketball
☐ Berlin
☐ Biology
☐ Boxing
☐ Breathing
☐ Buddha
☐ Building
☐ Bulgaria

Occurrences

Dogs were
domesticated
and soon
became man's
best friend,
apart from the
vicious ones
that didn't
like man at all.

An embarrassing moment

....
....
....
....

Doublers

Means of travelling
from A to B, but not C

☐
☐

The big deal

Wouldn't it be really
good if the cast of
Coronation Street turned
up at your house to...

☐

Sophistication gauge

None ● Mega

Mirror image

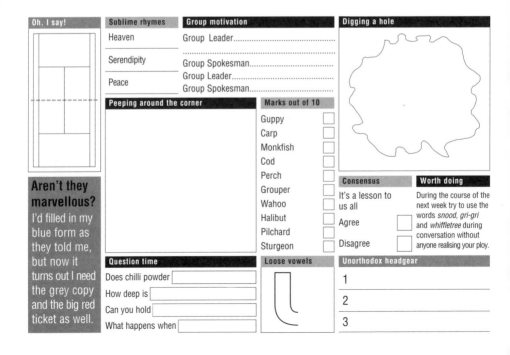

Oh, I say!

Aren't they marvellous?
I'd filled in my blue form as they told me, but now it turns out I need the grey copy and the big red ticket as well.

Sublime rhymes

Heaven

Serendipity

Peace

Group motivation

Group Leader...

Group Spokesman....................................
Group Leader...
Group Spokesman....................................

Peeping around the corner

Question time

Does chilli powder

How deep is

Can you hold

What happens when

Marks out of 10

Guppy ☐
Carp ☐
Monkfish ☐
Cod ☐
Perch ☐
Grouper ☐
Wahoo ☐
Halibut ☐
Pilchard ☐
Sturgeon ☐

Loose vowels

Digging a hole

Consensus

It's a lesson to us all

Agree ☐

Disagree ☐

Worth doing

During the course of the next week try to use the words *snood*, *gri-gri* and *whiffletree* during conversation without anyone realising your ploy.

Unorthodox headgear

1

2

3

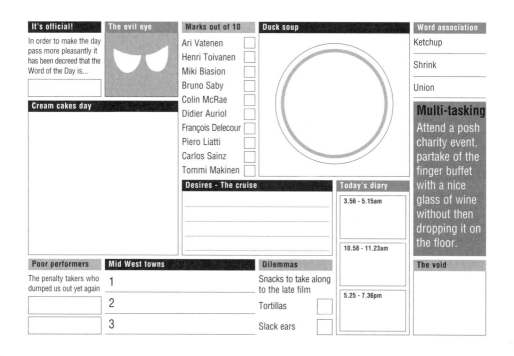

It's official!

In order to make the day pass more pleasantly it has been decreed that the Word of the Day is...

Cream cakes day

The evil eye

Marks out of 10

Ari Vatenen ☐
Henri Toivanen ☐
Miki Biasion ☐
Bruno Saby ☐
Colin McRae ☐
Didier Auriol ☐
François Delecour ☐
Piero Liatti ☐
Carlos Sainz ☐
Tommi Makinen ☐

Desires - The cruise

Duck soup

Today's diary

3.56 - 5.15am

10.58 - 11.23am

5.25 - 7.36pm

Word association

Ketchup

Shrink

Union

Multi-tasking

Attend a posh charity event, partake of the finger buffet with a nice glass of wine without then dropping it on the floor.

Poor performers

The penalty takers who dumped us out yet again

☐

☐

Mid West towns

1

2

3

Dilemmas

Snacks to take along to the late film

Tortillas ☐

Slack ears ☐

The void

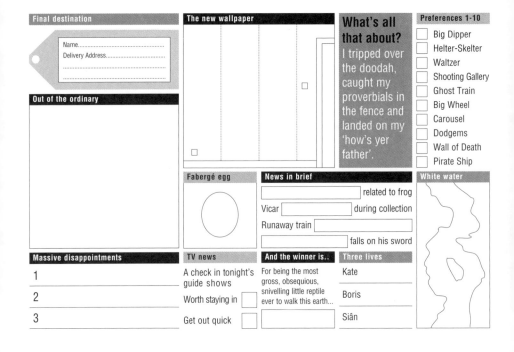

Final destination

Name...
Delivery Address.....................................
....
....

Out of the ordinary

The new wallpaper

What's all that about?

I tripped over the doodah, caught my proverbials in the fence and landed on my 'how's yer father'.

Preferences 1-10

☐ Big Dipper
☐ Helter-Skelter
☐ Waltzer
☐ Shooting Gallery
☐ Ghost Train
☐ Big Wheel
☐ Carousel
☐ Dodgems
☐ Wall of Death
☐ Pirate Ship

Fabergé egg

News in brief

☐─────────────── related to frog

Vicar ☐─────────────── during collection

Runaway train ☐───────────────

☐─────────────── falls on his sword

White water

Massive disappointments

1

2

3

TV news

A check in tonight's guide shows

Worth staying in ☐

Get out quick ☐

And the winner is..

For being the most gross, obsequious, snivelling little reptile ever to walk this earth...

Three lives

Kate

Boris

Siân

Kelvin

Felicity

Terry

The two week old milk in the fridge

Chuck it out ☐

Eat as yogurt ☐

1

2

3

W

Large piece of chalk and a small piece of cheese

Thought for the day

If the cap fits then it is far more likely to be worn, rather than not, although it does depend on the style.

☐ Billy Joel
☐ Sonny and Cher
☐ Simple Minds
☐ Bomb the Bass
☐ Cartoons
☐ Sweet
☐ Peter Andre
☐ Steeleye Span
☐ Jam
☐ Lisa Stansfield

P

Q

There was a catastrophic failure in security at the Palace today where police had to chase...

Tied up with string

To be considered

Having a crack at self sufficiency

Keep the patio ☐

Bring on the goat ☐

Recycling

To avoid having to undertake any major re-decorations, use a number of completed sheets to fill gaps and paper over the cracks.

Personal services

Classifieds

_____

_____

_____

_____

Toothy face

Basic instincts

1 _____

2 _____

3 _____

It's only D words

D

D

D

Flagrant abuse

_____ smells disgusting

_____ goes out with a right slapper

_____ has huge jug ears

_____ wears totally ridiculous clothes

Planned rumpy pumpy

Nooky

Mon Tues Wed Thurs Fri Sat Sun

Just saying

If you hadn't opened the cage door in the first place the budgie would never have flown straight into the window.

The village square

Marks out of 10

à la carte ☐

en croûte ☐

au gratin ☐

cordon bleu ☐

flambé ☐

table d'hôte ☐

provençale ☐

glacé ☐

jardinière ☐

au naturel ☐

Found
_____

Tight
_____

Rough
_____

Starter

Main Course

_____

_____

Dessert

_____

....
....
....
....

Marks out of 10

Slovakia	☐
Namibia	☐
Gibraltor	☐
Ireland	☐
Bhutan	☐
Madagascar	☐
USA	☐
Denmark	☐
Fiji	☐
Hong Kong	☐

Green vegetables

1 _____

2 _____

3 _____

Dilemmas

Are genetically
modified crops good?

Yeh, brilliant ☐

Ask my other head ☐

Finish it off

**Perfect
timing**

As the ignition
sequence
started the
Mission
Controller got
his cigarette
lighter ready,
just in case.

Options

Sensible or overkill in
trying to relax

Time to go

Rubber stamp

The committee concluded
that the person that they
would ask to open the new
prison block would be...

The void

- [ ] Schooner
- [ ] Raft
- [ ] Yacht
- [ ] Coracle
- [ ] Cruiser
- [ ] Kayak
- [ ] Supertanker
- [ ] Junk
- [ ] Canoe
- [ ] Sampan

Choose one

114   756

70   52

And now showing

A tale of intrigue and suspense in New Mexico

A bawdy romp through the area of Staines

A classic science fiction thriller set on Uranus

What a pane

Suggestive endings

ate

ed

ously

Security pass

Name

Position

Height

Visiting

A happy chappy

Fast drivers

1

2

3

Ask the audience

Send on the intriguing Master of Mime

Two hands [ ]

Two fingers [ ]

Wedding

Tackle

Today's noise

For today, or until a decision is made otherwise, the day's nominated noise is...

Behavioural problems

Those who attribute the term 'lifesaver' to someone who has just brought them a nice, hot cup of tea.

Preferences 1-10

- [ ] Archer
- [ ] Bonney
- [ ] Capstick
- [ ] Dunphy
- [ ] Fowler
- [ ] Heron
- [ ] Kernick
- [ ] Mingay
- [ ] Stephens
- [ ] Woodberry

The void

Fantasy concert ticket

This ticket enables

to go backstage at a concert by

The parrot of doom

Bouncing ball

First name terms

Gibbs

Watkins

Ramsey

Really good things to do

Things to do

Try to make everyone in the room feel uncomfortable about your behaviour at some point during the afternoon.

Blind date

Two rather sad people who deserve each other

Set squares

With hindsight

From day 1, it was obvious that it was asking for trouble not to wear a clown outfit to...

Dilemmas

Choosing a film to suit the boss

Love Actually

Die Hard

Bold as brass

1

2

3

Definitive definitions

[ ] (*n*) Rubbish bags after a dog's had a go at them

[ ] (*v*) To sit around in soaking wet clothes

[ ] (*v*) Getting stuck in a revolving door

What's on the box?

Sod's Law

I lovingly prepared all the kebabs, spent two hours trying to light the barbecue and now it's started to piss down.

Possessions

Pedal bin [ ]
Football [ ]
Masking tape [ ]
Compass [ ]
Cycle shorts [ ]
Feather duster [ ]
Digital watch [ ]
Nail clippers [ ]
Travel iron [ ]
Pressure cooker [ ]

In the mirror

Lewd thoughts

1 _____

2 _____

3 _____

The verdict

Losing bladder control in public

Guilty [ ]

Not guilty [ ]

Roll the ball

You what!?

So you're going to do no training whatsoever, put on a ridiculous animal costume that gets incredibly hot, then run for over 26 miles.

Nice logo

Location

Yesterday _____

Today _____

Tomorrow _____

What would happen?

[ ] + [ ] = [ ]

[ ] + [ ] = [ ]

[ ] + [ ] = [ ]

Holiday snaps

Card games

1 _____

2 _____

3 _____

The void

Dilemmas

Your dinner guest
for the evening

Laurel ☐

Hardy ☐

Marks out of 10

Muhammad Ali ☐

Pele ☐

Don Bradman ☐

Jack Nicklaus ☐

Jesse Owens ☐

Rod Laver ☐

Fangio ☐

Emil Zatopek ☐

Carl Lewis ☐

Babe Zaharias ☐

Crazy golf

The second half

Belt

Guide

Cream

Half and half

Thinking ahead

When trying to make a
really big effort to cook
and impress, always
avoid adding...

Instant favourites

Smell

Noise

Texture

Pairing up

Previous enemies who
are now good friends

Celebrations - An anniversary

....

....

....

....

What a total waste of time

Putting over
the virtues of
a really nice
Chianti to a
beardy real ale
drinker with a
stained, torn
jumper.

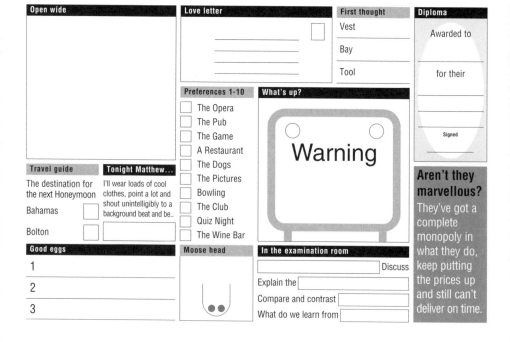

Open wide

Love letter

First thought

Vest

Bay

Tool

Diploma

Awarded to

for their

Signed

Preferences 1-10

- [ ] The Opera
- [ ] The Pub
- [ ] The Game
- [ ] A Restaurant
- [ ] The Dogs
- [ ] The Pictures
- [ ] Bowling
- [ ] The Club
- [ ] Quiz Night
- [ ] The Wine Bar

What's up?

Warning

Travel guide

The destination for
the next Honeymoon

Bahamas

Bolton

Tonight Matthew...

I'll wear loads of cool
clothes, point a lot and
shout unintelligibly to a
background beat and be..

**Aren't they
marvellous?**

They've got a
complete
monopoly in
what they do,
keep putting
the prices up
and still can't
deliver on time.

Good eggs

1

2

3

Moose head

In the examination room

Discuss

Explain the

Compare and contrast

What do we learn from

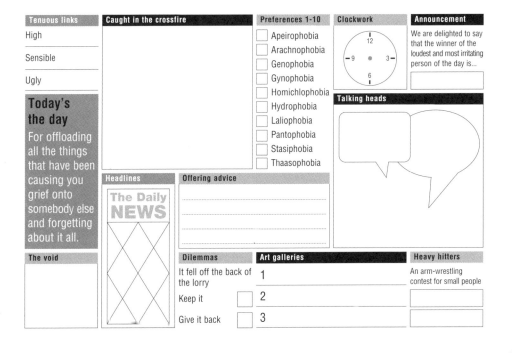

Tenuous links

High

Sensible

Ugly

Today's the day

For offloading all the things that have been causing you grief onto somebody else and forgetting about it all.

The void

Caught in the crossfire

Headlines

The Daily
NEWS

Preferences 1-10

☐ Apeirophobia
☐ Arachnophobia
☐ Genophobia
☐ Gynophobia
☐ Homichlophobia
☐ Hydrophobia
☐ Laliophobia
☐ Pantophobia
☐ Stasiphobia
☐ Thaasophobia

Offering advice

Dilemmas

It fell off the back of the lorry

Keep it ☐

Give it back ☐

Clockwork

12

9   ●   3

6

Talking heads

Art galleries

1

2

3

Announcement

We are delighted to say that the winner of the loudest and most irritating person of the day is...

Heavy hitters

An arm-wrestling contest for small people

Marks out of 10	
Roald Dahl	☐
Charles Dickens	☐
Ian Fleming	☐
George Orwell	☐
Frederick Forsyth	☐
Dick Francis	☐
Tom Sharpe	☐
Bram Stoker	☐
Ben Okri	☐
Rudyard Kipling	☐

What's all that about?

How long can you chew the cud, how heavy is kybosh and can you be hoisted on someone else's petard.

Call in for a quick one

Fingerprints

Name	Charge

Memory Lane

The eruption

Exercise regime

Pull [ ] behind your head

Do [ ] 50 times rapidly

Stretch [ ] over the table

Jump across [ ] for 20 minutes

Background music

Barely audible   Too piercing

Three Brians

Brian

Brian

Brian

Improvisations

Attempt to gather a group of people together as a herd by using the whistling and guiding techniques of an experienced shepherd.

Social stereotypes

1 _____

2 _____

3 _____

Drawing the line

Wearing your partner's underwear

Acceptable ☐

Not acceptable ☐

Great figures

2 2 2
6 6 6

Epic encounters

The very fast against the rather slow

Things that take 4 minutes

1
2
3

Best mates

Adam

Natasha

Daniel

Dilemmas

The best animal to keep as a pet

Elephant

Elephant Seal

Daylight robbery

It really could happen

Travelling on public transport will become so difficult and unpleasant that everyone will start using their cars.

Holding forth - Delayed flights

Tree surgery

Marks out of 10

Radar
Rain
Rowing
Relativity
Religion
Reptiles
Rice
Rockets
Romania
Rubber

Over-reactions

On launching the Titanic, the designer rose confidently to speak and declared it totally...

Forged signatures

Signed

Name in Block Capitals

The Void

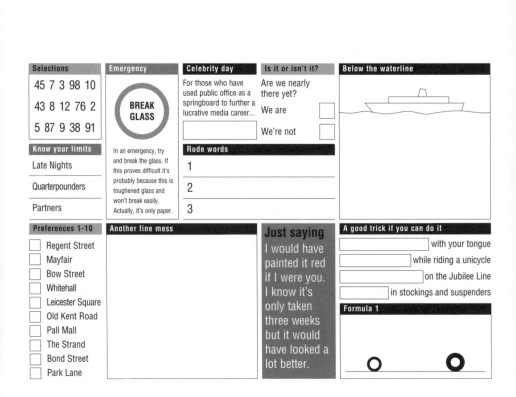

Selections

45 7 3 98 10

43 8 12 76 2

5 87 9 38 91

Know your limits

Late Nights

Quarterpounders

Partners

Preferences 1-10

- [ ] Regent Street
- [ ] Mayfair
- [ ] Bow Street
- [ ] Whitehall
- [ ] Leicester Square
- [ ] Old Kent Road
- [ ] Pall Mall
- [ ] The Strand
- [ ] Bond Street
- [ ] Park Lane

Emergency

BREAK GLASS

In an emergency, try and break the glass. If this proves difficult it's probably because this is toughened glass and won't break easily. Actually, it's only paper.

Celebrity day

For those who have used public office as a springboard to further a lucrative media career...

Rude words

1

2

3

Is it or isn't it?

Are we nearly there yet?

We are

We're not

Below the waterline

Another fine mess

Just saying

I would have painted it red if I were you. I know it's only taken three weeks but it would have looked a lot better.

A good trick if you can do it

with your tongue

while riding a unicycle

on the Jubilee Line

in stockings and suspenders

Formula 1

Stupid things to do

....
....
....
....

Olympic events

1 _____

2 _____

3 _____

Bad timing

On returning the
Doomsday Book very
late to the library the
lender was asked to...

The void

Official licence

Name

Licence

Purpose

Means the same

Actor

Genie

Resolve

Preferences 1-10

☐ William Blake
☐ Caravaggio
☐ Christo
☐ Tracey Emin
☐ El Greco
☐ Hans Holbein
☐ Lichtenstein
☐ Mondrian
☐ Rubens
☐ Turner

Choices

Animals to have to help
keep the lawn down

At the waterhole

The long lens

That'll be the day!

Everyone will
have a little
metal box on
wheels that
will take them
wherever they
want to go
quite quickly.

Dilemmas

To help freshen up
the house

Potpourri ☐

Pot Roast ☐

Shape It Up

The traditional beach dance during which the round bellied man attempts to change into his trunks with the aid only of a small towel.

Behavioural problems

Naming a baby after the place where they were conceived, the place they were born or the place from which they appear.

Mixed grill

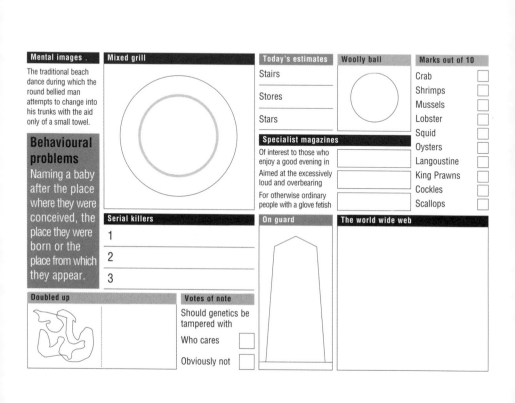

Serial killers

1

2

3

Doubled up

Today's estimates

Stairs

Stores

Stars

Specialist magazines

Of interest to those who enjoy a good evening in

Aimed at the excessively loud and overbearing

For otherwise ordinary people with a glove fetish

On guard

Votes of note

Should genetics be tampered with

Who cares

Obviously not

Woolly ball

The world wide web

Marks out of 10

Crab

Shrimps

Mussels

Lobster

Squid

Oysters

Langoustine

King Prawns

Cockles

Scallops

Did you know

When you are feeling ill or unwell you don't generally feel as good overall as you normally do when you're feeling better.

Mr or Mrs

Crystal

Taylor

Morse

Basic instincts - Sniffers

Boomerang

The void

Two for tea

Two friends for high tea at The Ritz

Name plate

Finding the spot

Living legends

1

2

3

Marks out of 10

Barley ☐
Maize ☐
Millet ☐
Oats ☐
Rice ☐
Rye ☐
Wheat ☐
Cotton ☐
Coffee ☐
Tea ☐

Empty boxes

Dilemmas

An addition to the dining experience

Puff Pastry

Puff Adder

You don't say

When getting dressed in the morning it is absolutely essential that you don't forget..

Back from the front

Preferences 1-10

- [ ] John McEnroe
- [ ] Steffi Graf
- [ ] Pete Sampras
- [ ] Monica Seles
- [ ] Bjorn Borg
- [ ] Venus Williams
- [ ] Roger Federer
- [ ] Martina Hingis
- [ ] Boris Becker
- [ ] Chris Evert

Sod's Law

The flight was delayed for 10 hours, the plane was then diverted to Beirut and now my bag's been found in New Delhi.

Definitive definitions

	(*n*) The light at the end of the tunnel
	(*v*) Trying to drink a thick milk shake through a straw
	(*n*) A three or five legged animal

Jail bird

Season's greetings

Suggestions box

An improved use for the Sahara Desert

Car Park ☐

A big sandcastle ☐

A great day out

1 _____

2 _____

3 _____

A nice pair

	+	
	+	
	+	
	+	

Feel good factor

Yesterday

Today

Tomorrow

Hammer time

12
9   3
6

Major incident

All hell broke loose when, during the changing of the guard, the commanding officer screamed...

Dilemmas	The void	Screen dogs	Spatial awareness

Dilemmas

Something to take to Ed's party

Buck's Fizz ☐

Buck Teeth ☐

Screen dogs

1

2

3

The first half

Road

Shower

Steering

Magic mushrooms

Preferences 1-10

☐ Galleon
☐ Frigate
☐ Liner
☐ Tall Ship
☐ Supertanker
☐ Steamer
☐ Dredger
☐ Junk
☐ Landing Craft
☐ Dragon Boat

Occurrences

A volcano erupted once causing dust and darkness to cover all the land until someone turned the light back on.

An embarrassing moment

....
....
....

The big deal

Wouldn't it be good if the World Formula 1 champion came round and asked you to...

Bliss gauge

Blissless   Yummy

Doublers

Ways of making a dull day much more splendid

Charting progress - Enthusiasm

Let's Go

| Mon | Tues | Wed | Thurs | Fri |

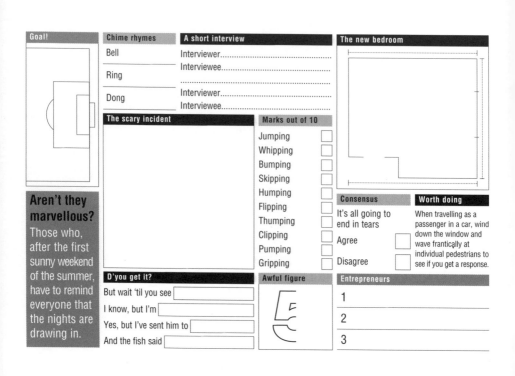

Goal!

Chime rhymes

Bell

Ring

Dong

A short interview

Interviewer..
Interviewee..
....
Interviewer..
Interviewee..

The new bedroom

The scary incident

Marks out of 10

Jumping
Whipping
Bumping
Skipping
Humping
Flipping
Thumping
Clipping
Pumping
Gripping

Consensus

It's all going to end in tears

Agree

Disagree

Worth doing

When travelling as a passenger in a car, wind down the window and wave frantically at individual pedestrians to see if you get a response.

Aren't they marvellous?

Those who, after the first sunny weekend of the summer, have to remind everyone that the nights are drawing in.

D'you get it?

But wait 'til you see

I know, but I'm

Yes, but I've sent him to

And the fish said

Awful figure

Entrepreneurs

1

2

3

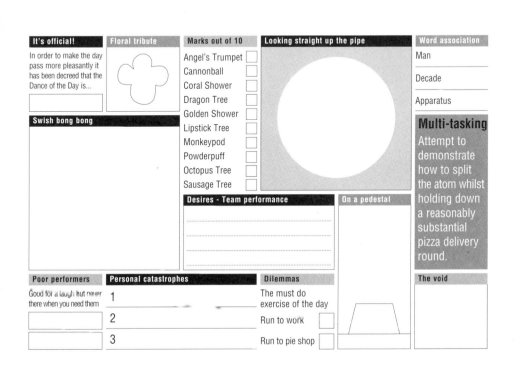

It's official!

In order to make the day pass more pleasantly it has been decreed that the Dance of the Day is...

Floral tribute

Swish bong bong

Marks out of 10

Angel's Trumpet ☐
Cannonball ☐
Coral Shower ☐
Dragon Tree ☐
Golden Shower ☐
Lipstick Tree ☐
Monkeypod ☐
Powderpuff ☐
Octopus Tree ☐
Sausage Tree ☐

Desires - Team performance

Looking straight up the pipe

On a pedestal

Word association

Man

Decade

Apparatus

Multi-tasking

Attempt to demonstrate how to split the atom whilst holding down a reasonably substantial pizza delivery round.

Poor performers

Good for a laugh but never there when you need them

Personal catastrophes

1

2

3

Dilemmas

The must do exercise of the day

Run to work ☐

Run to pie shop ☐

The void

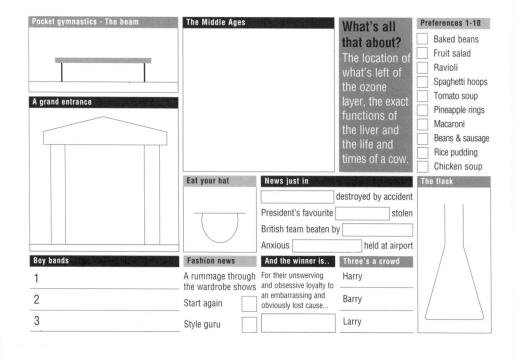

Pocket gymnastics - The beam

A grand entrance

Boy bands

1

2

3

The Middle Ages

Eat your hat

Fashion news

A rummage through
the wardrobe shows

Start again

Style guru

News just in

_____ destroyed by accident

President's favourite _____ stolen

British team beaten by _____

Anxious _____ held at airport

And the winner is..

For their unswerving
and obsessive loyalty to
an embarrassing and
obviously lost cause...

**What's all
that about?**
The location of
what's left of
the ozone
layer, the exact
functions of
the liver and
the life and
times of a cow.

Three's a crowd

Harry

Barry

Larry

Preferences 1-10

☐ Baked beans
☐ Fruit salad
☐ Ravioli
☐ Spaghetti hoops
☐ Tomato soup
☐ Pineapple rings
☐ Macaroni
☐ Beans & sausage
☐ Rice pudding
☐ Chicken soup

The flask

Star turns	Dilemmas	Spiders		Em	Poles apart

Star turns

Wendy

Gerald

Sandra

Dilemmas

The unwashed plates touch the ceiling

Wash Up ☐

Eat off the table ☐

Spiders

1

2

3

Em

M

Poles apart

Couldn't see eye to eye even if they had glasses

The void

Great events in history

Thought for the day

When the cat's away the mice will play and there won't be quite such a smell around the house until it gets back.

A face in the crowd

Preferences 1-10

☐ Ursula Andress
☐ Charlie Chaplin
☐ Joan Crawford
☐ Alec Guiness
☐ Deborah Kerr
☐ Jack Nicholson
☐ Gregory Peck
☐ Donald Pleasance
☐ Jane Russell
☐ James Stewart

Join the dots

Price fixing - I bought the car

Date

Pay

The Sum of   £

1345 673 2759 82

Bad behaviour

The date was cut short when Trevor insisted on showing Sally his huge collection of...

A wild hight

To be considered

Putting your shirt on a dead cert

You bet ☐

No chance ☐

Recycling

Soak the sheet in water, squeeze it up into a ball and hurl it very hard at the outside wall of your house as a substitute for pebble-dashing.

Notice board

The Week AHEAD

Angry face

It's only T words

T

T

T

Big hits

1

2

3

What's the use?

☐ with a frying pan

☐ in a barrel

☐ with an ice pick

☐ in a pith helmet

Caffeine intake

Stimulation

10.00 11.00 12.00 13.00 14.00 15.00 16.00

Just saying

You can say what you like, Mr Pig, but building your house out of straw wasn't the best decision you've ever made.

The expedition

Marks out of 10

Hankies ☐

Golf Balls ☐

CD ☐

Tie ☐

Mug ☐

Book on Sport ☐

Gadget ☐

Video ☐

Socks ☐

The Procrastinator ☐

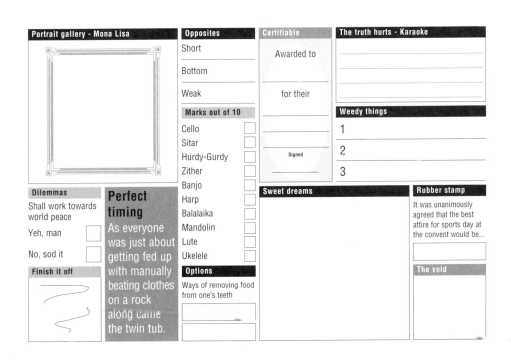

Portrait gallery - Mona Lisa

Opposites

Short

Bottom

Weak

Certifiable

Awarded to

for their

The truth hurts - Karaoke

Marks out of 10

Cello

Sitar

Hurdy-Gurdy

Zither

Banjo

Harp

Balalaika

Mandolin

Lute

Ukelele

Signed

Weedy things

1

2

3

Dilemmas

Shall work towards world peace

Yeh, man

No, sod it

Finish it off

Perfect timing

As everyone was just about getting fed up with manually beating clothes on a rock along came the twin tub.

Options

Ways of removing food from one's teeth

Sweet dreams

Rubber stamp

It was unanimously agreed that the best attire for sports day at the convent would be...

The void

☐ Bourbons
☐ Rich Tea
☐ Custard Creams
☐ Hobnobs
☐ Ginger Nuts
☐ Digestives
☐ Garibaldi
☐ Chocolate Fingers
☐ Wafers
☐ Jammy Dodgers

Choose one

69 · 333
88 · 3

RSVP

A request to appear in the church pantomime ☐

Asked to ride on a small scale yellow road train ☐

An invitation to appear on a TV game show ☐

A great ending

_____ ous

_____ ly

_____ ion

A long and dangerous journey

Today's person

For today, or until a decision is made otherwise, the day's nominated person is...

☐

Behavioural problems

A colleague who fawns all over the boss in a totally undignified manner, particularly when it works.

Through the microscope

Driving test

Mindless activities

1 _____

2 _____

3 _____

Ask the audience

Raymondo and his novelty trousers

Pull 'em up ☐

Debag him ☐

Belly

Dancer

Preferences 1-10

- [ ] Begonia
- [ ] Bell Flower
- [ ] Busy Lizzie
- [ ] Dahlia
- [ ] Edelweiss
- [ ] Foxglove
- [ ] Goat's Beard
- [ ] Hollyhock
- [ ] Lupin
- [ ] Sunflower

The void

Fantasy day permit

This permit entitles the bearer to

_____

_____

_____

Lasts for one day only

The grim reaper

Egghead

Really good things to do

First name terms

Murphy

Findlay

Reed

Blind date

The walking ego and
the shrinking violet

Things to do

Walk down to the shops wearing huge clown shoes and try not to step on any of the cracks in the pavement or dog doings.

Square deal

With hindsight

At the Royal Gala it would have been better not to have asked the Queen to sit in the...

Dilemmas

A takeaway to match the mood

Chinese

Indian

Very nice biscuits

1 _____

2 _____

3

Definitive definitions

[ ] (*n*) Hugely disappointing quiz show prizes

[ ] (*v*) Attempting to run with flippers on

[ ] (*adj*) A teacup after a storm has been in it

Late night TV

Sod's Law

I set off early on a two hour drive, made sure I was there in plenty of time and I've now been told that it's been cancelled.

Possessions

Drinks mats [ ]
Model boat [ ]
Bulldog clip [ ]
Thermometer [ ]
Badminton racket [ ]
Clothes brush [ ]
Egg poacher [ ]
Swiss Army knife [ ]
Biscuit tin [ ]
Dictionary [ ]

The big picture

Inadvisable holiday destinations

1 _____

2 _____

3 _____

The verdict

Pretending to win having cheated _____

Guilty [ ]

Not guilty [ ]

Dropping the bomb

You what!?

We're going to conduct a survey, listen to what people have to say, draw some conclusions and then do something completely different.

Political logo

Frisky feelings

Yesterday

Today

Tomorrow

The sum of the parts

[ ] − [ ] − [ ] − [ ] = [ ]

[ ] + [ ] + [ ] + [ ] = [ ]

[ ] − [ ] − [ ] − [ ] = [ ]

Very bad make up

Good hats

1

2

3

The void

Dilemmas

Your dinner guest for the evening

Noel Gallagher ☐

Liam Gallagher ☐

Marks out of 10

Aeroplane ☐
Barometer ☐
Camera ☐
Chocolate ☐
Detergent ☐
Electric Guitar ☐
Linoleum ☐
Pencil ☐
Rocket ☐
Tampon ☐

Day nursery

The second half

Sign

Cleaner

Green

Half and half

Thinking ahead

When planning a long night of partying, always remember to take a spare...

What a total waste of time

Trying to book an appointment with the doctor to examine and diagnose a complaint before it goes away again.

Reality check

Time	Place
Who's in front	
Who's behind	
Who's talking	

Pairing up

A wrinkled red thing and a huge blue thing

Celebrations - Passing the exam

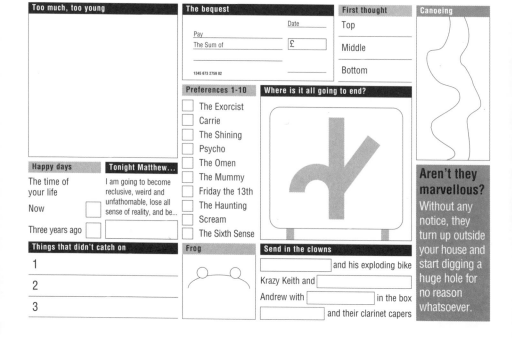

Too much, too young

Happy days

The time of your life

Now

Three years ago

Tonight Matthew...

I am going to become reclusive, weird and unfathomable, lose all sense of reality, and be...

Things that didn't catch on

1

2

3

The bequest

Date

Pay

The Sum of   £

1345 673 2759 02

Preferences 1-10

☐ The Exorcist
☐ Carrie
☐ The Shining
☐ Psycho
☐ The Omen
☐ The Mummy
☐ Friday the 13th
☐ The Haunting
☐ Scream
☐ The Sixth Sense

Frog

First thought

Top

Middle

Bottom

Where is it all going to end?

Send in the clowns

and his exploding bike

Krazy Keith and

Andrew with   in the box

and their clarinet capers

Canoeing

Aren't they marvellous?

Without any notice, they turn up outside your house and start digging a huge hole for no reason whatsoever.

Tenuous links

Deep

Family

Stinky

Today's the day

For going home, having a wash and brush up, a quick bite to eat, then going out all night on the lash.

The void

Motherhood and apple pie

Headlines

The Daily
NEWS

Preferences 1-10

- [ ] Dick Francis
- [ ] Bram Stoker
- [ ] Catherine Cookson
- [ ] Gerald Durrell
- [ ] Frederick Forsyth
- [ ] Arthur Hailey
- [ ] Stephen King
- [ ] George Sand
- [ ] Fay Weldon
- [ ] Jules Verne

Offering advice

Dilemmas

Choice of clothes for the evening

Black tie ☐

Black mini ☐

Decision time

Announcement

We trust that you enjoy this evening's play where the really annoying cow will be played by...

The broken mirror

David Bowie hits

1

2

3

Heavy hitters

Suggestions for the duel at dawn

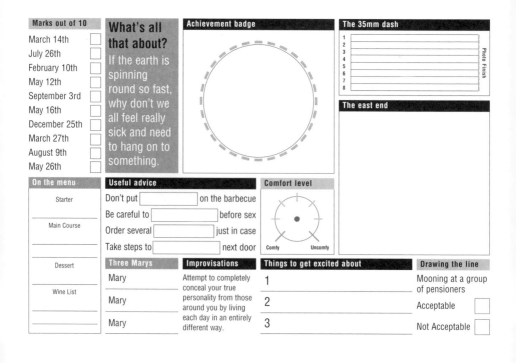

Marks out of 10

- March 14th ☐
- July 26th ☐
- February 10th ☐
- May 12th ☐
- September 3rd ☐
- May 16th ☐
- December 25th ☐
- March 27th ☐
- August 9th ☐
- May 26th ☐

What's all that about?

If the earth is spinning round so fast, why don't we all feel really sick and need to hang on to something.

Achievement badge

The 35mm dash

1
2
3
4
5
6
7
8

Photo Finish

The east end

On the menu

Starter

Main Course

Dessert

Wine List

Useful advice

Don't put [_____] on the barbecue

Be careful to [_____] before sex

Order several [_____] just in case

Take steps to [_____] next door

Comfort level

Comfy   Uncomfy

Three Marys

Mary

Mary

Mary

Improvisations

Attempt to completely conceal your true personality from those around you by living each day in an entirely different way.

Things to get excited about

1

2

3

Drawing the line

Mooning at a group of pensioners

Acceptable ☐

Not Acceptable ☐

Great figures

53
20

Epic encounters

Two loud mouths see who is the loudest

Boxers

1

2

3

Best mates

Blodwen

Eugene

Ruth

Dilemmas

Cleaners needed after the weekend

Industrial

Home help

Mini beasts

It really could happen

People will recognise that experimental art has great innovative benefit even if they don't like it themselves.

Holding forth - Computer crashes

Coming over the horizon

Marks out of 10

Apes
Badgers
Caterpillars
Dolphins
Geese
Hippopotami
Jellyfish
Peacocks
Sheep
Trout

The Void

Over-reactions

On completing the new Millennium Bridge the architects and designers declared it to be...

Letter of complaint

Selections

π ¥ Δ
Ω √ ∂
μ ® ¬

Time trials

Dressing

Salad Dressing

Undressing

Preferences 1-10

☐ Jelly
☐ Chockie Bikkies
☐ Cake
☐ Sausage Rolls
☐ Blancmange
☐ Crisps
☐ Iced Gems
☐ Snowballs
☐ Cheesy Things
☐ Sweets

Panic alarm

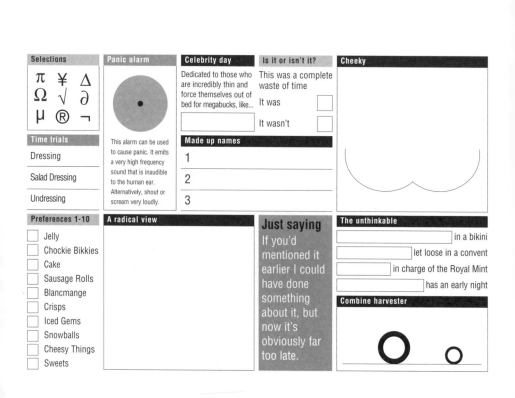

This alarm can be used to cause panic. It emits a very high frequency sound that is inaudible to the human ear. Alternatively, shout or scream very loudly.

A radical view

Celebrity day

Dedicated to those who are incredibly thin and force themselves out of bed for megabucks, like...

Made up names

1

2

3

Is it or isn't it?

This was a complete waste of time

It was ☐

It wasn't ☐

Just saying

If you'd mentioned it earlier I could have done something about it, but now it's obviously far too late.

Cheeky

The unthinkable

_____ in a bikini

_____ let loose in a convent

_____ in charge of the Royal Mint

_____ has an early night

Combine harvester